LYCOPTOS

A COMPARATIVE STUDY
OF THE WAYS
OF IBERIAN WOLVES
IN THREE CAPTIVE PACKS

Robert Lyle

1998

First published 2000
Published and distributed by:

The Wolf Society of Great Britain
49 Foxhill Road
Reading
RG1 5QS
UK

www.wolfsociety.org.uk

ISBN 0 9534735 1 1

Printed with the financial support
of the Bernd Thies Foundation,
Basle, Switzerland

Printed in the UK on environmentally friendly
paper by Conservatree Print and Design

About The Author

Robert Lyle was born 1920 and educated at Uppingham. He studied composition under Herbert Howells at the Royal College of Music before joining the army in 1940, serving with the 1st Armoured Division, Intelligence at GHQ Cairo, and with 18 Army Group in North Africa. After the war he worked in P.R. and journalism, He entered the Subud Spiritual Association in 1960, moving to Italy. Published works include '*Mistral*' (C.U.P. 1953 and Aliscamps, Paris 1994), '*Subud*' (S.P.I. 1973), and '*A Way Through The World*' (Altamira, Netherlands, published in English and Dutch). Robert moved to Portugal in 1963, where he began to study wolves in 1983, and founded the Iberian Wolf Recovery Centre in 1989, retiring as director in 1996. He has published numerous articles on wolves and been the subject of television features worldwide.

Dedicated

to

Francis Dubois

and

Frank Van Meulebeke

of the

International Wolf Federation,

and

João Francisco

of the

Iberian Wolf Recovery Centre,

True Friends

of

The Wolf

Acknowledgements

I wish to express my thanks to Dr Carlos Magalhães who introduced me to the Mafra wolves, to Ing. João Bugalho, who authorised my visits, and to the staff of the Tapada who gave me every assistance.

Respecting the Malveira wolves my thanks are due first of all to the memory of Bernd Thies whose legacy, mediated by the Foundation which bears his name, ensured the reception and survival of the wolves at the IWRC. Secondly, I wish to thank Mr Hermann Hirzel, then President of the Bernd Thies Foundation, for his unfailing support and understanding which made possible the provision of suitable, naturalistic enclosures for the wolves, of great benefit to them as wolves and as subjects of this study.

I extend heartfelt thanks to Richard Morley, who has given much time and energy to overseeing the printing and production of my book and doing all the work ill-health has prevented me from doing, and to my daughter, Virginia, for her careful proof-reading.

I further wish to thank Prof.Dr. Jan van Haaften for kindly reading and commenting on my typescript and, last but not least, Dr Ueli Halder for his appreciation which led to the sponsorship of this study by the Bernd Thies Foundation of which he is currently the Manager.

It would not be appropriate to thank the wolves but my profound and lasting gratitude will, I hope, be evident from the text.

Preamble

This study sets out to describe and compare the behaviour of three packs of Iberian wolves, (*Canis lupus signatus*) captive in large, naturalistic enclosures, protected from interference and, therefore, able to fulfil most of their social and biological functions.

It begins with short histories of each pack and with descriptions of the locations and of the individual wolves. It then proceeds to summarise the observations made of the behaviour of each pack under the appropriate headings - "Pack formation, evolution and structure", "Courtship and breeding", etc., each section being completed by a commentary.

The Mafra Pack (MI) was observed over a period of six years (January, 1985 to March, 1991); the first Malveira Pack (MIIA) was observed and socialised with almost daily for five years (June, 1991 to January, 1997); the second Malveira Pack (MIIB) likewise (from 1994 to January, 1997).

MI was (and still is) located in the National Game Reserve at Mafra, near Lisbon, known as the Tapada de Mafra. MIIA and B were (and still are) located in the Iberian Wolf Recovery Centre (IWRC) at Val da Guarda, adjacent to the Tapada.

The study is biased by my total rejection of cartesian mechanistic behaviourism. Currently, "science" has tended to become a science of measurement. What cannot be measured, by one means or another, does not exist or, at best, can be disregarded. I cannot accept this tendency which, so as to achieve a neat but spurious "order", leaves out much that is real and vital. It also leads to accusations of anthropomorphism. This is a much used and abused anathema - (the parallels between modern scientists and mediaeval scholastics are most revealing). In fact I do recognise that animals and humans differ, not only in degree, but in one essential respect. The animal nature is static, the human, dynamic. In other words, the animal form and its content invariably correspond, while we cannot assume that a human form promises a human content. This is why animals, unlike humans, are neither "good" nor "evil" - they can *be*, but they can never *become*.

It follows that my observation of the ways of these wolves has been neither ethologically orthodox nor sentimental - an interesting word which means "feeling with the mind". I came to the work without preconceptions but with love, which alone can open the windows of understanding. Konrad Lorenz shocked his fellow scientists when he asserted that one cannot hope to understand any animal unless one can love it. The meaning of this is that one cannot understand - as opposed to gathering and analysing data - without becoming one with one's subject, and one cannot become one with one's subject unless one can love it. To this heresy I plead guilty.

Robert Lyle
August, 1999

Contents

Part I

Pack Histories

My regular observations of this pack began in January, 1985, but I first visited the wolves' enclosure in November, 1984.

There were then four animals, two males and two females, all 18 months old. The pairs were littermates, males and females being unrelated. The females, whom I named Musca and Carina, had been there for some months; the males, Deneb and Neb, had only just been introduced. All four had been born in captivity.

(The facility had been set up by a Portuguese biologist, with the object, I was told, of studying inbreeding, but the study was never pursued and, apart from the provision of food and water, the wolves were left to their own devices.)

The sisters appeared mutually tolerant. The brothers, on the other hand, were on very friendly terms although, from the first, Deneb showed himself to be dominant. The males - but not Musca - chased Carina regularly, thus relegating her to the omega position and, in the Spring of 1985, it was clear that Deneb had chosen Musca as his mate; thus she became the alpha female.

Although mating took place between the alphas that Spring no pups were born. In 1986, however, Deneb and Musca, now three years old, mated successfully and Musca gave birth to a litter of four pups, all of whom survived. There were two males, Hamal and Rigel, and two females, Ara and Vega.

Neb, the beta male, was removed from the enclosure in March, 1987, to take part in a Forestry Services exhibition at Silves in the Algarve. The exhibition passed off without incident, but on the return journey Neb attempted to escape by gnawing a hole in his crate, or maybe only to get more air as it was a very hot day. When the men who were transporting him stopped for lunch at Evora in the Alentejo, they noticed the hole, nailed a board over it and went away to eat. On their return they found Neb dead from asphyxiation.

Although Deneb and Musca mated again that year no pups were born or, at least, none survived. Then, in November, 1987, Deneb died of unknown causes. Thus the pack lost its two adult males in the same year.

After Deneb's death Musca assumed the leadership of the pack, a position she held until after the mating season in 1988, when Hamal and Ara were established as the alphas and the breeding pair, Rigel as beta male and Vega as the subordinate female. Musca went into honourable retirement and Carina remained the omega wolf. At that time Musca and Carina were five years old and Musca's offspring two years.

Despite their youth Hamal and Ara bred successfully and Ara gave birth to a litter of pups believed, at first, to consist of three or four animals, but only two survived more than three weeks and one of these two subsequently died, leaving one survivor, Altair.

Carina, omega wolf as ever, was much more severely harassed by the younger wolves than she had been by Deneb and Neb. In January, 1989, she was found dead in the enclosure by Services personnel from Lisbon, but her body was not removed for analysis and a subsequent search, in which I took part, found no trace of her; the cause of her death therefore remains unknown and mysterious, if not suspicious.

In the Spring of 1989 there were therefore six survivors in the enclosure: Musca, aged six; Hamal, Ara, Rigel and Vega, aged three, and one yearling male, Altair.

The alphas mated again in March, 1989 and Ara gave birth to her second litter in May. Musca was this time relegated to a subordinate position, together with Vega, but no wolf was made to occupy the omega position vacated by Carina's death.

Of that year's litter five pups - probably the entire litter - survived. The two males were named Algol and Thuban; the three females Muscida, Capella and Sulafat.

In the Spring of 1990 only one male pup - Regulus - was born (or survived) and, as soon as he had left the den he was always seen in the company of his very solicitous father, Hamal. Thuban, a very beautiful animal, became the beta male.

In October of the same year, in an unfortunately careless manner, six of the wolves - Hamal, Ara, Thuban, Rigel, Altair and Sulafat - were moved to the Lisbon Zoo where they were accommodated in penal conditions.

Almost at once Vega assumed the leadership of the remnant pack and held this position until the Spring of 1991 when she was ousted by the new alpha pair, Algol and Muscida, and driven down again to a very subordinate position together with the solitary yearling, Regulus - who, until then, had enjoyed her protection - who became the omega animal. At this time, too, Musca, always aloof and for some time ailing, died.

In the Summer of 1991, Vega and Regulus both escaped from the enclosure by scrambling up a corner post and over the top into the main, walled Game

Reserve (of c.900 hectares) probably in flight from severe harassment.

Regulus was soon sighted, shot at and wounded and, as he was never seen again, presumably died as a result.

Vega survived for several months until she was shot dead by the same ranger who had wounded Regulus acting on instructions from the Director of the Hunting Services (Serviços de Caça).

MIIA

The six initial members of this pack were littermates, born in the wild in the Spring of 1991. They were rescued by a Portuguese biologist, Luís Miguel Moreira, when their mother was found dead from poison, and hand-reared until they were c.six weeks old, when they were transferred to the Iberian Wolf Recovery Centre.

In the Autumn of 1991 they were moved into a large enclosure, by which time their SRO was clearly established, with Sandalo and Morena, alpha male and female; Manchas, beta male; Fosco and Mouro, subordinate males, and Clarinha, the subordinate female.

Very early in 1992 harassment of Clarinha, initiated by Morena, began and by February had become so severe that she had to be removed.

No pups were born that year - the alphas were still yearlings.

In April of 1992 five members of the pack escaped and were at large for a few hours but they did not go far, returned when they were called and were easily persuaded to re-enter the enclosure. Manchas did not join in this escapade but all six were temporarily removed to the Lisbon Zoo while the fence of their enclosure was repaired and reinforced.

While they were lodged at the Zoo Morena came into oestrus and, as they had not been segregated, she and Sandalo mated.

During that Spring and into the Autumn harassment of Mouro began and gradually increased until by the end of the year it was very severe and he was ostracised.

Early in 1993 Mouro was moved to an adjacent enclosure (C4) from which, at the onset of the mating season in his natal pack he escaped, remained at large for some seven months and was finally shot - the evidence is circumstantial - by a hunter from Lisbon.

That same Spring Morena gave birth to a litter of four pups: Nimbo, a male; Bruma, Zef and Neblina, females. In the Winter of 1993 Bruma and Neblina were harassed and both were subsequently and intermittently candidates for the omega position.

In 1994 Sandalo, Morena and Manchas were moved to the adjacent enclosure (C4) so that repairs to their own enclosure could be carried out. Manchas was almost immediately severely harassed and ostracised by the alphas and, when the three of them were moved back, Manchas became the omega wolf, persecuted not only by the alphas but also by Fosco. Two weeks later his removal was seen to be essential and he was transferred to C4, now occupied by Clarinha, with whom he quickly formed a close bond - and the nucleus of a new pack, MIIB (see below).

That same year Morena contracted an infected uterus, was removed and operated. She had to be kept in isolation for several months and when she was finally returned was rejected by her ex-mate, Sandalo and by the new beta, Fosco.

In the Spring of 1995 Sandalo mated with Neblina who gave birth to a litter of four pups - three males, Onor, Alvão, Douro; and one female, Alva, - but no close bond between Sandalo and Neblina resulted and Neblina reverted to a subordinate position as soon as the pups were old enough to fend for themselves.

During the Winter of '95/'96 Sandalo and Fosco were vasectomised. They spent a week in isolation, recuperating, during which time Nimbo - who earlier had risen to dominate Fosco - took over the leadership. On their return, however, he omitted to make sufficiently abject submission to Sandalo and was driven down to the omega rank where he remained until he was finally removed - to join Morena - in the Winter of '96/'97.

In the Spring of 1996 Sandalo mated with Zef who had risen through the female ranks to become alpha but, as he had been vasectomised Zef did not become pregnant. Although no close bond resulted, Zef remained alpha female.

At the beginning of 1997 the MIIA SRO was: Sandalo and Zef, alphas; Onor and Fosco, beta and gamma males; Douro and Alvão, sigma or subordinate males; Bruma, sigma (or subordinate) female; and Neblina, omega.

At this writing (May '98) the SRO is unchanged.

MIIB

This pack was formed by human intervention in 1994 when Manchas was removed from C3 and joined Clarinha in C4.

Their close bond resulted in successful mating in 1995, when Clarinha gave birth to a litter of six pups - Dourado, Nemrod, Órion, males, and Risca, Aurora and Serena, females. Four of them - Nemrod, Órion, Aurora and

Serena - were removed at two weeks old to be hand-reared. The intention had been to remove all the pups but Clarinha succeeded in relocating two of them - Dourado and Risca - before any of the staff reached the den.

Early in 1996 Manchas was temporarily segregated (he was lodged with Morena) as a contraceptive measure, but this was done too late. (He was in fact vasectomised in August.) He had already mated again with Clarinha who duly gave birth to a second litter of six pups - Prado, Feno, Teixo and Zimbro, males; Murta and Aura, females. This time the first five were removed to be hand-reared, Aura being left to console her mother.

In the summer of 1996 the SRO was: Manchas and Clarinha, alphas; Dourado, beta; Aura, gamma female and Risca, sigma, and it was seen to be unchanged in the Spring of 1997, in which year, Manchas having been vasectomised, no pups were born. It is still stable now (May,'98) with no omega animal.

The Locations

The wolves' enclosure, which still exists and is still occupied by descendants of the original alpha pair, is situated in a remote part of the 900 hectare National Game Reserve (A Tapada de Mafra). A concrete-based, chain-link fence encloses a 1 hectare area of open grassland, patches of heather scrub, a number of pine, cork, olive and hawthorn trees. In the centre a large stone circle gives onto a wooded glen, thickly overgrown with brambles. Relatively sparse when observations began, the vegetation - and especially the brambles - grew extensively over the years, providing additional cover for the wolves, but making it harder to observe them.

The area slopes downhill from the fence on three sides, to the stone circle and the glen. Water is provided in a concrete trough near the only gate. The soil is clay and in Winter pools and puddles form, but in Summer the area is very dry, although there is abundant shade.

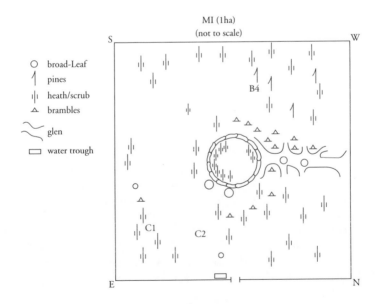

MIIA

In contrast to the MI enclosure, which is a square (100m x 100m), that of MIIA, built in 1991 on land belonging to the Swiss-based Bernd Thies Foundation, is in the form of an irregular octagon enclosing c.13,000m². The form was dictated both by the exigencies of the terrain - the side of a valley, steep in parts - and by a wish to provide the wolves with a less rigid boundary to their "territory". It provides excellent cover and variety, having two heaths, woods of pine and eucalyptus, this last undergrown with brambles, and an open, grassy slope. The reinforced chain-link fence was eventually lined by a five-strand electric fence after escapes had shown the chain-link fence to be fallible. This enclosure is referred to as "C3" (Cercado no. 3).

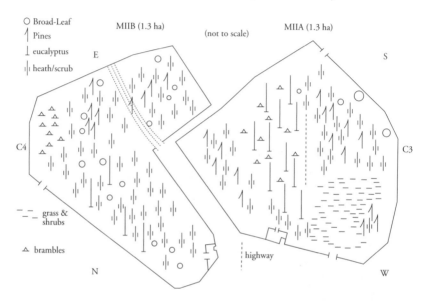

MIIB

This enclosure ("C4"), adjacent to C3, is roughly L-shaped and is an irregular decagon, enclosing c. 13,000m². In other respects, too, it is similar to C3, but the heather is more extensive, there are fewer eucalyptus and brambles and there is no open grassy slope, so that observation is more difficult as the heather is dense and very high; but it is ideal for the wolves. The fencing arrangements are as for C3. In both, bowls provide drinking water and there is a small concrete pool in which the wolves can lie and take a bath in hot weather.

The Wolves

The wolf of the Iberian Peninsula is a sub-species of the European Grey Wolf (*Canis lupus lupus*) and is known as *Canis lupus signatus*. Rather smaller and lighter than the Grey Wolf, Signatus is 70-80cm high at the shoulder and weighs 30-35kg, but larger and smaller specimens have been described. (Both these limits will be significantly exceeded by some of the subjects of this study.) The colour of its pelage runs from almost white through grey and grizzled to various shades of brown. There are russet patches behind the ears and lighter patches on muzzle and throat. Legs and underbelly are fawn. The eyes are oblique and pale yellow, but amber eyes sometimes occur.

2. Individually

2a: MI

Deneb, the alpha male until his death in November, 1987, was grizzled, with a light-brown face without distinguishing marks. His legs were short and out of proportion. He was strong and sturdy and, in maturity, probably weighed c.35kg. (I had no possibility to weigh the wolves in MI and the staff of the Reserve never did so.)

Deneb's brother, Neb, beta male until his death in March, 1987 was taller than Deneb, i.e., his legs were of normal length, and his pelage was a striking silver-grey. He was a very handsome animal and, being of a quite different colour from all the others, was always easy to distinguish.

Musca, the alpha female until she relinquished her post to Ara in 1988, was a rich brown colour. A dark mark ran from her forehead to her muzzle and, as her rather close-set eyes were outlined with black her face appeared as if marked by a cross. The white marking on the lower muzzle and throat, characteristic of this sub-species, spread considerably over the years to cover most of her face until she became instantly recognisable. In addition, her right ear was slightly kinked.

Musca's sister, Carina, all her life the omega animal, was a slightly darker brown which at times took on the hue of chestnut leaves in Autumn, but the white mark on muzzle and throat was much less noticeable. She was a little larger than Musca who, like her mate Deneb, was stocky. To begin with the sisters were very alike, but they became easily distinguished as time passed and

Musca's appearance changed.

When the alpha pair's four pups were nine months old they were as large, although not as massive as the adults. A wolf's head, in particular, seems not to fill out until the animal is three years old, but a broadening of the face was apparent by the time they were a year old; this was especially pronounced in the male yearlings, Hamal and Rigel. (In my opinion the best way to judge a wolf's age is by the ratio: ear-length/cranial volume; for the ears grow much faster. Thus a young wolf has a small face and long ears, while in the adult the face has filled out to alter the proportions.) Colour is also a way to estimate age, but I do not think it is so reliable. At five weeks the pups were dark brown; until their first moult they were dark grey; thereafter they showed the various combinations of grey, brown, buff and fawn characteristic of the sub-species, dark grey predominating along the spine and fawn on the underparts. All four of the second generation had the dark frontal mark, inherited from their mother. Rigel was browner than the other three - he was almost bronze - and his face was dark. Hamal and Ara (allowing for bimorphism) were very alike, but Hamal was larger and his face was broader. In both, grey predominated over brown. Ara resembled Hamal and Vega but her face was more uniformly dark and her ears were longer.

Altair resembled his mother, but with a lighter face and shorter muzzle. He was further distinguished by clearly defined markings on his face, back and tail.

The pups of Ara's second litter were surprisingly varied. The body of the largest, Algol, was light brown, as was his face. The next largest, Thuban, was by contrast grey, with dark markings and a dark dorsal stripe. Muscida was the darkest of the three females. Capella was brown and Sulafat grizzled.

All had - typically of Iberian wolves - dark streaks down their forelegs, black-tipped tails and yellow eyes.

2b. MIIA

Sandalo is grizzled, a mixture of grey, brown and fawn. As a pup he was the colour of sandalwood - hence his name.

Morena is dark grey, the most nearly monochrome of her litter.

Fosco is and Mouro was darker than the others, a contrasting mixture of black and fawn. Onor resembles Sandalo, Nimbo is more like Morena. Bruma is grizzled, Neblina, brown. Zef is grizzled with grey shades predominating. Douro has a black face. Alvão and Alva resemble Neblina. Mouro had one yellow and one amber eye; the others have strikingly clear and piercing yellow eyes.

Sandalo weighs c-36kg, Morena only 27kg. Fosco is and Mouro was slightly smaller than Sandalo. Douro and Alvão are as big as their father; Alva a little larger than Morena.

2c. MIIB

Manchas, although formerly only beta to Sandalo's alpha, is bigger than his brother, nearer to 50kg. His coat is also more reddish brown. Clarinha is light brown and weighs much the same as Morena (c.27kg). Dourado is the same size as Fosco (c.35kg); Risca as Clarinha; Aura is a little larger than her mother. All have yellow eyes. Risca is darker than Dourado and Aura takes after her mother. Clarinha's other offspring, who were removed, are not described as they do not fall within the scope of this study.

The individual characters of our dramatis personae will emerge as we proceed.

Part II

1. Pack Formation and Structure

MI

When observations began in January, 1985, the pack was still unformed. As all four animals had been separated from their parents at an early age - parents who had also been born in captivity - they had had no experience of family or pack life to guide them. They had to start from scratch.

To begin with the females kept together or, at least, apart from the males, while Deneb and Neb were always seen together and appeared to be inseparable. Tail positions and general deportment, in the absence of agonistic actions or displays, indicated that Deneb was the dominant of the two males.

The relationship between the sisters was less clear. They were hard to observe, being very shy but, as the males regularly chased Carina around the area, I assumed that she had been cast in the role of peripheral or omega wolf and that Musca would in due course become the alpha female.

The pack structure crystallised with the onset of the breeding season in the Spring of 1985. Deneb was clearly alpha male and pack leader, Neb the beta. Carina was confirmed as the omega, not by any action on her sister's part but by the males' on-going "persecution". These positions were confirmed by the traditional deportment and tail positions of all the wolves. (Only Musca's restraint vis-à-vis her sister was not "traditional".) Finally, Deneb and Musca mated, confirming their status as the alphas and breeding pair.

Although it is generally held that the social ranking order (SRO) in a pack is composed of two ranking orders (RO), i.e., male and female, determined unilaterally according to sex [1], this was notably not the case in this pack until 1988. For the first three years it applied only to the males. No action that could be interpreted as an assertion of dominance or gesture of submission was observed to take place between the females until 1988 and their relative positions in the female RO were evident only from their tail positions and the behaviour of the males towards them.

In a large pack, in addition to the alpha animals there are, first a group of sub-dominant (gamma) wolves below the top-ranking animals, and a second group of juveniles (delta) below the sub-dominants [2]. In this pack, for much of the study period, there were only the alphas, the beta male, and a group of

12

four deltas who were three years younger than their parents but who, after the death of Deneb and Neb, automatically rose in the hierarchy.

Deneb and Musca failed to breed successfully in their second year and I am inclined to believe that a litter born to Musca in her fourth year died before the pups were weaned: they may even have been stillborn (v. infra). The SRO at the time of the breeding season in 1985, when all four animals were two years old, was therefore:

A	Deneb	Musca	
B		Neb	
O			Carina

It remained thus until August, 1985, when Carina attacked her sister whom I saw with two wounds, one on her back and one on her rump, and for a time it seemed as if Carina had succeeded in displacing the alpha female. No further agonistic actions were observed, however, and it soon became apparent that the males and, in particular, the alpha, Deneb, had not accepted the new situation. At first they seemed puzzled and disturbed spectators, but they finally intervened. They resumed their pursuit of Carina and went to some pains to keep her away from Musca. As a result the original SRO was restored and thereafter remained stable until Deneb's death in late 1987. This was a clear and apparently unusual case of the males interfering in and determining the female RO.

After the pups were born in May, 1986, an embryo RO was observed among them, irrespective of sex, when they were five months old. It had probably been visible earlier, but my observations were interrupted during August and September while I awaited the renewal of my permit. No agonistic actions among the pups were to be expected at that stage and I saw none, but Rigel, by virtue of his greater initiative, seemed mildly dominant. In second place came his sister, Vega; in third place his other sister, Ara, and lastly, his brother, Hamal, who regularly submitted when chased by the others during play sessions. No other submissive behaviour, either active or passive, was observed among the young wolves, either when they were pups or, later, when they were yearlings. This situation only changed after Deneb's death.

Then, in the Spring of 1987, when the young became yearlings, Hamal, who hitherto had been the most timid of the four and had increasingly absented himself from play sessions and social activities - to such an extent that at one time I thought he had died - suddenly grew in physical stature and initiative. Again, I saw no conflicts or displays but, by the time the yearlings were 14 months old, Hamal appeared to have become the leading (rather than the "dominant") yearling, while Ara was demoted to last place. She was not harassed in any way, however; on the contrary, all four, when seen together, were clearly on very friendly terms. Ara, however, spent much time with her mother.

The SRO in September, 1987, was therefore:

A	Deneb	Musca
B	—	
D	Hamal, Rigel	Vega, Ara
O		Carina

It will be recalled that the beta male, Neb, died after his removal in March, 1987. This tragedy not only deprived the alpha male of a constant companion and loyal "lieutenant" - a deprivation somewhat alleviated by the onset of the breeding season (which nevertheless was unsuccessful) - it also meant that Deneb assumed sole responsibility for the protection of and good order in the pack. Some months would elapse before the yearlings began to keep him company and assist in the "control" of Carina.

I did not expect the beta position to be filled until the Autumn of 1987 at the earliest. It seemed probable that Rigel would be Neb's successor, not least because Deneb seemed to be taking a special interest in his development, but the alpha's death in November completely altered the situation. At first, Musca assumed the leadership but, after the 1988 breeding season, when Hamal clearly established his dominance on the male side and mated with Ara (with whom he had been "going steady" for several months), Musca gradually and voluntarily relinquished her position as pack leader to Hamal and, as alpha female, to Ara. Musca went, as it were, into honourable retirement, but she continued to act as a kind of general supervisor - as "elder" - until just before the mating season in 1989, when the alphas, then three years old, no longer allowed her to interfere.

In the Spring of 1989, the SRO was, therefore:

A	Hamal	Ara
B	Rigel	
G	Altair	Musca, Vega

There is no omega in this SRO as Carina died in January, 1989 and, for some time, was not replaced.

Five pups - Algol, Thuban, Muscida, Capella and Sulafat -were born in 1989 and, during the following Autumn and Winter, Rigel was demoted and his place was taken by Altair; Musca became more solitary and, apparently of her own accord, lived on the edge of the pack, while Vega became the omega animal. The onset of the 1990 breeding season saw a further change, when Thuban rose to become beta and Altair became subordinate. In the Summer of 1990 the SRO was:

A	Hamal	Ara
B	Thuban	
G	Altair, Rigel	
D	Algol	Muscida, Capella Sulafat
S	Regulus	

Regulus being the only (surviving) pup of that year.

As already stated, six of the pack were removed to the Lisbon Zoo in October, 1990. The choice of victims was indiscriminate and the removal of the alphas and the beta male ensured the maximum amount of disruption. Algol and Muscida finally emerged as the alphas; Vega and Regulus took to flight (only to be shot in due course), and Musca died quietly, unnoticed and alone.

MIIA

The six pups were 6+ weeks old when they arrived at the IWRC. From the first Fosco and Clarinha - but especially Fosco - were more timid than their siblings and were prompted to take cover by the unexpected or unfamiliar. To begin with, Mouro seemed to be the candidate for dominant male but after a short time he began to be harassed by the others and was then found to have an abdominal hernia, a defect which, detected by the wolves before it was seen by Ros Lewis, who had come to give a helping hand, evidently accounted for the change in behaviour.

Mouro was removed, operated, convalesced in my house and was duly returned to the pack, there to take up a subordinate status, thenceforward and for a long time disputing the delta male rank with Fosco. In his place and immediately after his removal, Sandalo rose to the embryo alpha rank in which he was later confirmed and has held, undisputed, ever since. At the same time Manchas assumed the role of beta.

On the female side Morena quickly emerged as dominant, firmly relegating Clarinha to what turned out to be the lowest ranking though not, as yet, the omega animal.

All this happened during the first few weeks when the pups occupied -two small, adjacent, interconnected, "quarantine" enclosures (combined area 200m^2). When, at five months of age, they were moved into C3 (13,000m^2), this SRO was maintained; it merely became more visible. For example, I used to enter the enclosure, socialise with the wolves and then take a walk through the heaths and woods. I was always closely followed by the whole pack. The wolves fell in behind me in line-ahead formation and, invariably, in strict hierarchical order; Sandalo - Morena - Manchas - Mouro/Fosco - Clarinha.

Pack formation in MIIA was fairly straightforward and took place with little conflict; it was also very rapid as though its elements were destined for their roles, in accordance with Rochefoucauld's profound maxim: *Character is destiny.* The SRO remained stable after both Clarinha and Mouro were removed, i.e., until the demotion and subsequent removal of the beta male, Manchas in 1994.

During the temporary sojourn of Sandalo, Morena and Manchas in C4 their triadic relationship broke up. The alphas - Morena being the more insistent - suddenly turned against Manchas and forced him into complete isolation - we had to try to feed him separately. I advised that he should be left behind when the time came to return them to C3, but my advice was overruled by the biologists who were constrained by their preconceptions of wolf behaviour and, as a result, and as already reported, Manchas was returned only to become the pack's new omega, necessitating his subsequent removal.

Until this time Manchas had formed part of the ruling trio, often though not always accompanying the alphas on their patrols and during their siestas out in the open. His place was duly taken by Fosco who proved to be a more tentative and "canny" occupant, a wolf who, since his earliest days, had used his intelligence to adapt to the various problems and challenges of wolf family life.

(While Sandalo, Morena and Manchas were absent in C4, Fosco confidently assumed the leadership, even challenging Sandalo across the track which separated their territories but, as soon as Sandalo was returned, Fosco tactfully made immediate submission and thus avoided the fate which overtook Nimbo later on. So, always ready to take a vacant position, he was equally ready to beat a strategic retreat, melt into the background and lie low until the threat had vanished.)

The SRO in the Summer of '93 after the birth of Morena's first and last litter was:

A	Sandalo	Morena
B	Fosco	
G	Nimbo	
D		Bruma, Zef, Neblina

and it stayed that way until Morena's illness and departure, a much more serious kind of disruption (v.infra.).

But, although Sandalo subsequently mated, first with Neblina and then with Zef, neither of these rose to take Morena's place (Zef came closest to doing so) not only, if at all, in my view, because they were Sandalo's offspring, but because Sandalo was inhibited by the very close bond he had formed with Morena which was, in effect, irreplaceable.

Neblina could be considered alpha female only for a few months, more by courtesy of her maternity than for any other reason. Briefly, therefore, in 1995, the SRO became:

A	Sandalo	Neblina
B	Fosco	
D	Nimbo	Zef
S	Onor, Douro, Alvão	Alva
O		Bruma

and the year after it had changed to:

A	Sandalo	Zef
B	Fosco	
G	Onor	
D	Nimbo, Alvão	Alva
S		Bruma
O		Neblina

The pivot and anchor of the whole pack had become and remains Sandalo. The beta rank was unstable after Manchas's demotion and remained ill-defined until 1998. During '96-'97 Nimbo challenged and ritually defeated Fosco. Fosco, as usual when in trouble, "exiled" himself, but Nimbo did not succeed to the beta position because of the unexpected rise of Onor who owed his rapid promotion to his father's evident favouritism and protection (v. infra). He was thus, despite his immaturity, in effect the beta male. But, when Sandalo and Fosco were removed, vasectomised and returned, Nimbo, lacking Fosco's diplomatic skills, was hunted into the omega position by Sandalo and subsequently persecuted so severely that he was removed in January '97.

In the Spring of 1997 the SRO was therefore:

A	Sandalo	Zef
B	Onor	
G	Fosco	
D	Douro, Alvão	Alva
S		Bruma
O		Neblina

MIIB

This pack formed in 1994 when Manchas joined Clarinha in C4 where, after a few days' hesitation they became inseparable companions and then, the following year, a very closely bonded pair, producing litters of six pups in 1995 and 1996. As four of the pups were removed in '95 and five in '96, human interference had a much greater effect on pack structure in this case than in either of the others. For one thing Clarinha's maternal burden was greatly eased; for another, competition was greatly reduced.

In the Summer of '95 Manchas and Clarinha were, as usual, almost always together and as time went by they were often accompanied by the male pup, Dourado, and less frequently, but regularly, they were joined by the female pup, Risca.

In the Summer of '96 Aura, the sole survivor of the "raid" on the den, having received her mother's exclusive care and attention, grew quickly and displaced Risca in the ruling quartet. Although Risca was sometimes seen with the other four she usually either preferred or was ordered to remain aloof, but the treatment she has so far received does not justify an omega classification. Therefore MIIB's SRO, in 1997/98, is:

A	Manchas	Clarinha
B	Dourado	
G		Aura
S		Risca

Commentary

In principle packs form in three stages: a pair bond; a nuclear family; and an extended family, the third stage being potential since its occurrence depends upon the presence of various factors. There are then two post-formation stages, generally dependent on the occurrence of stage three: these are dispersal and repetition.

In captivity this more or less orderly progression is inevitably endangered by limitations of space and by human interference, e.g., the removal of omega animals or pups from the den.

The three stages in our study were most nearly realised in MI, but the removal of omega animals can to a certain extent be considered equivalent to enforced dispersal since, in the wild, these wolves would have left the pack, either to trail it or to go off in search of a territory of their own, and so, with reservations, MIIA can be thought of as adhering to our model. Not so MIIB unless the removal of the pups is taken to simulate the death of most of the pups in two successive litters due to disease or predation - today, a not unlikely scenario.

In the widest sense, then, we can say that the formation of our three packs basically adhered to a naturally occurring model, especially if we equate human interference - benevolent in all but one of these cases - with known natural happenings, hazards or calamities.

Each pack began with a firm pair-bond: Deneb-Musca; Sandalo-Morena; Manchas-Clarinha. The first was ended by Deneb's death, but Musca, who survived her mate by four years, never mated again. The second was ended by Morena's illness and removal, but Sandalo subsequently mated with two of his daughters (by Morena) in successive years, although no close bonds were formed. The third - Manchas-Clarinha - survives, having, at this writing (05.'98) lasted four years and appears to be as strong as ever.

Nuclear families were formed in all three packs, although limited in size by human interference in MIIB. Some mortality occurred in MI but not in MIIA or B. Similarly, extended families - with the same reservation in the case of MIIB - were formed by second generation mating in MI; by two successive changes of breeding female in MIIA; and continuously and monogamously only in MIIB.

The alphas, or one of them, together or apart, constitute the king-pin of the pack, having normally emerged as the most suitable through a process of testing, of challenge and response, a process which, nevertheless, seems subject to predestination. In our case Manchas and his eventual mate Clarinha were the exceptions: both are ex-omegas; both were removed. Manchas had established himself as beta male while still a pup but lost the position three years later, suddenly and for no discernible reason, but Clarinha had occupied the lowest rank from the start. Yet their subsequent management of their own pack, with the proviso that this was made easier by human intervention - it is easier to raise one than to raise six pups - has been exemplary.

Deneb and Sandalo, on the other hand, although both were smaller than their beta companions, were from first to last outstanding alphas (as Sandalo still is). "Born leaders", in both cases their deportment indicated innate authority and self-confidence, although this took a sterner form with Sandalo perhaps because he was born in the wild and therefore that much closer to the "source".

The female alphas were less obviously predestined, with the exception of Morena who, despite an inherited heart-murmur was from the beginning until her forced exclusion, undisputed Queen. Musca was surprisingly tolerant and pacific - even when she assumed the leadership she was rarely and then only mildly disciplinary - and she was the exception in another way. It is generally held that the SRO is established bilaterally, the alpha male being responsible for the male side, his mate for the female, and this has held good for MIIA and B. But in MI it was not so. Deneb was responsible for both. Musca not only forwent this functional privilege, she never joined in any of the numerous actions against her sister whose omega status was determined entirely by the males of the first generation and then by the whole pack - other than Musca herself - after the birth of the second and third.

The subordinate SRO is more complex. The first generation pups born to Deneb and Musca, unlike Sandalo et al, took months to establish their SRO - but Sandalo's family group were orphans. In MIIA there have been constant changes among the sigmas. Bruma and Neblina have alternated and Zef rose from near omega to the alpha position.

The strangest variation observed, however, has been the rise of Onor. While still a young pup, only recently weaned, and unlike any of his siblings - or uncles and aunts - he accompanied his father and would come down and even, though unhabituated, take food from my hand and, when only a little older, would not only drive his great-uncle, Fosco, away from the food but would take meat from under Sandalo's nose, an impertinence no other wolf would have dared to commit. Thus protected, he leap-frogged over his siblings and elder relatives into what was - is - the beta position, spending more time in the alpha's company, on patrol or at rest, than any other wolf. Apart from his great-uncle, Fosco, and his uncle, Nimbo, there were two other males in his litter, Alvão and Douro, both larger than he, so his preferment must be attributed not just to supposedly innate superiority but more to his father's particular and indulgent fondness for him, thus introducing a new and emotional factor into the determinants of the SRO.

Similarly, though less oddly, Aura, in MIIB, by force majeure a lone pup, rose over the yearling Risca to become her mother's regular companion; but the fact that she was a lone pup and therefore received her mother's (and father's) full attention as well as an abundance of nourishing food, makes her pre-eminence more understandable than Onor's.

2. Courtship and Mating

MI

From the end of January 1985 on, Deneb paid much attention to Musca. There was an increase in olfactory signs and "readings" both of urinations and of Musca's anal and inguinal regions. I did not witness any act of copulation but their behaviour suggested that these had taken place during the second week in March; they spent long periods together under cover in the glen, abstained from food and, when they finally emerged, kept company more closely and frequently than before.

Neb paid little attention to Musca but he showed some interest in Carina. On one occasion, apparently sexually aroused, he approached her but was rejected with a snarl. A few days later, however, I saw her present to him, raising her tail and holding it to one side, indicating that she was receptive; but no act followed and I think none occurred, probably because Neb was still sexually immature (although at that time all four animals were just two years old); he may also have been inhibited by his beta rank. It is well known that the alpha pair are commonly the only pair to mate and ensure that this is the case by preventing others from mating, but in this case neither Deneb nor Musca made any attempt to "discipline" Neb or Carina.

Despite the obvious marital bond Musca did not become pregnant that year. The bond, too, became gradually more attenuated, although it never disappeared, after the end of the season when Deneb returned to the company of his brother whom he had temporarily abandoned. I surmise that the strong bond which unites the breeding pair and has been attributed to the length of the copulatory tie [3], may depend at least as much on the conception of pups, that is, on breeding success.

The same pattern of courtship was repeated the following year, but it was more intense and Neb paid less attention to Carina who did not come into oestrus; her sexuality appeared to have been suppressed, probably due to the stress of her social role. This time Deneb and Neb were very active in keeping her away from Musca. Again, however, Musca herself made no attempt to control or otherwise interfere with her sister's actions or to prevent her having contact with Neb, and in this respect Deneb was equally tolerant.

Mating between the alphas took place between 10 and 15 March. During those few days, so far as I could see, Deneb stayed with his mate in the denning area, only emerging briefly to warn Neb or Carina away if they approached the glen. Neither Deneb nor Musca appeared to take any food during this time.

This year, too, a much stronger bond was formed between the alphas after breeding (all the wolves were now three years old); they were seen together much more, although often accompanied by Neb, who remained on very friendly terms with both of them.

Musca showed no signs of pregnancy until the beginning of May. Then her mate became very solicitous for her welfare. When food was left in the enclosure he would take pieces to her and stand by her while she ate them before feeding himself. At the same time, with Neb's help, he took care to keep Carina away from her. Breeding was successful this year and resulted in a litter of four pups: Hamal, Rigel, Vega and Ara.

In 1987 courtship seemed less intense than in the previous year, possibly because Neb had been removed - never to return - just before the alphas mated, but also, no doubt, because they now enjoyed a secure relationship. Mating took place between 22 and 27 March, ten days later than in 1986 and, therefore, I expected another litter to be born during the last week in May, but something went amiss and there were no pups. The odd happenings which occurred at the anticipated moment of birth are described in the next section.

Regular friendly "get-togethers" (Adolf Murie) were frequently seen during all three of these courtship seasons, involving the alphas and the beta male. Carina was excluded from such sessions during these periods but was sometimes included in get-togethers at other times of the year. During these sessions the males paid much attention to Musca, standing one on each side of her, pressing her flanks and caressing her. Except on three occasions - to be described - Deneb permitted Neb's full participation.

Deneb's death in November of that year created a completely new and open situation. The pack had to undergo a restructuring to provide a new, stable SRO and to give rise to a new breeding pair. Musca had taken over the leadership and the last few weeks of 1986 passed quietly. I expected changes with the turn of the year, but the wolves were surprisingly quiet during January, February and the first three weeks of March. On 25 March a brief courtship season began. There were three observed confrontations between the two surviving males, Rigel and Hamal, involving bared teeth and growling, but these did not escalate and were broken off inconclusively. The object of their attentions and rivalry appeared to be Vega who was approached and followed by both males but by Rigel in particular. I was in fact expecting Rigel to become the new alpha male and to mate with Vega.

I was wrong. Three days later the situation had changed radically. Hamal had successfully challenged Rigel for the alpha position, as was evident when Rigel submitted to his brother as soon as Hamal silently bared his teeth, at which Rigel lay down and raised a leg in the air in token of his submission.

Moreover, Hamal now carried his tail in the alpha position while Rigel bore his between his legs. Rigel, on the other hand, had sprained his left hind-leg and was limping badly and this may have forced him to give way during the unobserved but decisive confrontation. There were no marks or wounds on any of the animals except Carina who was now subject to more severe harassment than she had ever suffered under Deneb's rule. Vega, too, was now marginalised and she and Rigel kept apart. The object of Hamal's sexual interest was not Vega but Ara, with whom he had in fact being "going steady" for many weeks. He followed her continually and was seen to try to mount her on 29 March but, on that occasion she, being still unreceptive, rejected him.

The next day tensions in the pack seemed to have relaxed. Rigel kept to himself and rested his leg as much as possible. Vega also roamed on her own. Carina was no longer being harassed; she moved freely about the area, often in Musca's company, but with her tail in the omega position. Musca, for her part, had abandoned her aloof stance. She had accompanied her offspring during their courtship activities, which were closely connected with the establishment of the new SRO and, as soon as the breeding season began, had trotted busily around the area, smelling the tracks and tufts of grass to obtain the information she needed.

Hamal was always seen in Ara's company and they finally retired to the denning area. On circumstantial evidence I assumed mating to have taken place for the first time on 29/30 March although, owing to their immaturity, I thought reproduction unlikely. Vega's sexuality, after Rigel's defeat, seemed to have been suppressed and at no time did either male show any sexual interest in Musca or in Carina. The latter's sexuality was again suppressed, presumably due to social stress, while Musca's was equally inhibited, probably due, in her case, to the loss of her mate.

On that same day I witnessed an unusual gathering of all four females. Carina stood beside her sister, Musca, who ignored her, while Ara lay down in submission to her mother. Vega was less respectful and Musca asserted her authority by mounting Vega and growling.

Carina's reprieve did not last. She was again marginalised and Vega, too, became peripheral. Musca, when she led the pack out, was accompanied only by Hamal, Ara and Rigel. All except Hamal, who was respectfully affectionate, submitted to Musca when she approached them, but Rigel no longer made submission to Hamal; he either stayed aloof or accompanied the mated pair.

The harassment of Carina was suddenly resumed. This was initiated by Hamal, supported by Ara and Rigel. Carina was badly bitten. Her old wound was reopened and extended across her rump just above the tail. Vega, too, was bitten, almost certainly by Ara, but only mildly; she had a red bite-mark on her left haunch.

Despite this persecution Carina persisted in following Vega and eventually mounted her, making thrusting movements. At first Vega was compliant and held her tail aside as though Carina were a male, but later she tried to avoid her aunt's attentions. Immediately after that first mounting had taken place, Hamal, Ara and Rigel rushed out from cover and fiercely attacked both females, forcing them apart and driving them right across the enclosure. These attacks were repeated every time Carina attempted to mount Vega.

Two days later, on 6 April, Carina was still following Vega about, but by then the harassment (in which, as usual, Musca took no part) had become sporadic and at one moment Musca led the whole pack, including Carina, across the open field. All harassment seemed to have ended by 8 April. Carina had ceased to opportune Vega. Hamal and Ara were confirmed as the mated pair but now, the season being over, they were often accompanied by or rested with Musca and Rigel.

Musca still remained alone at the head of the hierarchy, but Rigel and Vega appeared to be denied the denning area which for some time remained the preserve of Musca, Ara and Hamal. Ara asserted her dominance over Vega quite often; Hamal his over Rigel very rarely. On social occasions, however, all five animals (Carina once more being always excluded) could be seen amicably together and ritual threats and submissions were in abeyance.

Courtship and breeding in late Winter and early Spring, 1989, were orthodox, the breeding pair being securely established and the SRO firm. The only change occurred with the onset of the breeding season in March. Musca began by reassuming her supervisory role of the preceding year, but her time for retirement had come and Hamal now took charge of the pack. When Musca attempted to interfere she was quietly but firmly escorted by Hamal to a particular area of the enclosure, to which she was more or less confined until the end of the season, after which she regained her freedom of movement but not her authority. She was relegated, with Vega, to a subordinate position. Throughout she behaved with her usual dignity and calm. She had revealed the latent strength of her character when she took over the leadership after Deneb's death, and she showed it again now, by her serene acceptance of demotion.

This season, too, the alphas kept Rigel and Vega firmly apart. They themselves mated successfully in the third week in March and on or about 20 May Ara gave birth to a litter of five pups. When they were grown, in the Winter of '89/'90, they joined the adults - all but Rigel - in harassing Vega who became the omega wolf after Carina's death, although her trials were much less severe.

Courtship and breeding in 1990 were untroubled, but only one pup,

Regulus, ever appeared and, as soon as he was free of the den was seen constantly in his father's company. Hamal showed him every care and attention, perhaps because he was an "only pup". But, sadly, they were separated in October, when his father and five others were removed. For a time he enjoyed Vega's protection but, as already described, was the following year forced to escape with her, only to meet an early death at the hands of man.

MIIA

There were no signs of pre-mating activity in 1992. In March all the wolves were ten months old, a month in which five of them escaped and were at large for a few hours but were easily recaptured.

The season in 1993 was exceptional in that the pack, less Mouro who had escaped, had to be moved to the Lisbon Zoo while the fencing of both large enclosures was reinforced. Mouro's escape, from the adjacent enclosure, may well have been prompted by the threats of the males, especially Sandalo, in C3, and this in turn may have been prompted by the approach of oestrus in both Morena and Clarinha.

When I visited the wolves in the zoo they were so stressed by the conditions that at first they did not recognise me and only Sandalo greeted me. Nevertheless Morena did come into oestrus and she and Sandalo duly mated. On the return journey an ecograph was taken of Morena's heart which confirmed that she had a congenital heart murmur.

Next year the alphas and Manchas had to be temporarily transferred to C4 and, as it had been decided to limit reproduction, Morena was given a contraceptive injection before the move. This method, which the vet considered 96% successful in the case of domestic dogs, did not work for Morena who came into oestrus in March and Sandalo duly mated with her on the 17th.

After repeated matings by the alphas Fosco also attempted to mate with Morena who, as it happens, had also shown a fondness for him. The first time, Morena rejected him with a snarl. The second time Sandalo rushed up and drove Fosco away. The third time, with Sandalo lying down thirty metres away and probably exhausted, Fosco was successful: the tie lasted eight minutes. Thereafter Fosco kept company with the alphas and seemed to be an established member of the dominant trio.

In May it was clear that Morena had not become pregnant, and, as described above, she was eventually moved for examination and found to have an infected uterus.

In 1995, "courtship" was marked by vigorous efforts by Sandalo to prevent liaisons while he himself showed no interest in any of the remaining females - who were his daughters.

Neblina was seen to be in oestrus on 12 March but when, on that day, she presented to Sandalo, he rejected her with a snarl. He avoided Neblina for several days, rejecting her if she approached him but, apparently because natural instinct was too strong for him, he succumbed and mated with her on 17 March. No bond was formed however and, after accompanying her for a few days, he left her to her own devices and resumed his solitary habits.

The following year Zef, until then the most unobtrusive of the females, had superseded both Neblina and Bruma and in due course Sandalo, showing a little more interest in her than he had in Neblina, mated with her. Sandalo had previously been vasectomised, as had Fosco, so no pups were expected. Unlike Neblina, however, Zef did retain her alpha status and enjoyed an easy, if rather distant relationship with Sandalo.

In February, 1997, a new management was installed by the Bernd Thies Foundation and no observations were carried out either then or in 1998.

MIIB

Initially this pack consisted of a single pair, Manchas and Clarinha. Almost from the start of their relationship constantly together, courtship in 1995 was simply an intensification of their feeling for each other. As said above, a plan to prevent mating by segregating them failed because they pre-empted it.

Although constantly at her side, not only during the few days of mating but throughout her subsequent pregnancy, Manchas did not show much concern for Clarinha until near to the time of her confinement. Unlike Deneb, or Sandalo, he did not allow her priority when food was provided until near the time of giving birth.

The following year Manchas was removed to be vasectomised but, once again, those responsible miscalculated: mating had already taken place. When Manchas was tranquillised Clarinha, despite her obvious fear, stayed with him until the last moment and then, when he was removed, uttered a piercing wail which left no one who heard it in doubt as to the depth of her relationship with Manchas or the intensity of her anguish, all the worse for their having been torn apart at the height of their "honeymoon".

Commentary

To describe this period in MI required much more space than for the same in MIIA, while MIIB needed only three paragraphs. The reason is simple and instructive. In MI the SRO was severely disrupted by the death of the alpha male and his beta in the same year. There followed an interregnum dominated by the surviving alpha female and then there was a further serious disruption when the alphas were removed to the Zoo.

In MIIA on the other hand, although Morena, the alpha female, had to be removed, the pack's alpha male, Sandalo, has held undisputed sway from the beginning and continues to do so at this writing (5. '98).

In MIIB the period has been correspondingly even more straightforward: both alphas have been in command from the outset until now.

This underlines the importance of continuity in the stability and survival of wolf packs and the danger of disruption by illness, accident, or, especially, human interference. This is a further reason why "control" of wolves in the wild by hunting is unacceptable and why "control" of any kind is likely to be unproductive as well as unethical.

Of the three cases, it is noteworthy that both Deneb and Sandalo were solicitous for the welfare of their mates during their pregnancy, while Manchas was not, or was noticeably less so. Of the three Deneb was the most caring. Both Deneb and Sandalo were evidently conscious of their mates' condition long before it was so to a human observer, while Manchas appeared to be oblivious until near the end of the period. That they were in fact aware of this state seems to be confirmed by Sandalo's behaviour during the second season when Morena did not become pregnant - and he did not take her food or allow her priority.

3. Denning, Birth and Pup-rearing

MI

In the first year, 1985, Musca sited the den under a hawthorn tree in a thick clump of brambles at the south-west edge of the glen. It was very well chosen, being the place offering the most protection and concealment in the whole enclosure. It remained in use thereafter and so became traditional, but, admittedly, alternative sites would have been less satisfactory.

That year no pups were born. Musca's first litter was born during the week-end of 18/19 May, 1986. For the next month no sounds at all were heard from the denning area and the mother was only rarely seen when she came out for a short rest or to eat. Food was placed not far from the den by Deneb and Neb; the meat was not cached, only relocated. The father was not allowed near the den for the first two weeks after birth but spent his time with his brother.

I first saw the pups five weeks after they were born, when they emerged from the den, one by one. Their ears were already stiffening but they were still unsteady on their legs and did not venture far. They romped together, on this occasion watched over by their father who, when he saw me in the heather on the ridge above, quickly shepherded them back to the den.

Two days later they emerged again, this time with their mother. Deneb was lying down nearby. Musca stood in front of the gap that leads to the glen and they suckled. She remained standing, raising a leg and her tail to accommodate them. One fed after the others and, to judge by Musca's expression, caused her some pain.

In fact they were weaned shortly afterwards and began to eat meat brought to them and regurgitated by their parents and, occasionally, by Neb. During this period, from June until the end of July, when my visits were temporarily suspended while I arranged an extension to my permit, the adults, with the exception of Carina, whose attentions were not permitted, were very solicitous for the pups' welfare. If I was sighted they were shepherded away to a safe distance and Neb would warn them of danger by giving a series of "wuffs".

From their first appearance in the open the pups played together, but they became more independent as time passed. Three of them - Rigel, Vega and Ara - spent more time together and interacted more often. Hamal frequently did not appear at all and seemed to be weaker and more timid than the others.

They grew rapidly and at three months were already very active, exploring the area and gradually extending their range. At that stage, however, their explorations were supervised by Deneb and Neb, who discouraged them from entering the exposed area past which humans usually approach.

Supervision was relaxed by the time the pups were five months old and from then until the next breeding season in 1987 they became progressively more independent, both of their elders and of one another. At first I thought this independence reflected contemporary behaviour in the wild in Portugal, where the pack was no longer an extended family but had been reduced to the mated pair and their pups of the current year, or to a mated pair or even to solitary wolves [4], but their subsequent behaviour did not support this interpretation; as time passed they drew closer together, first to one another and then, after Neb's death, to their father as well.

Musca became pregnant again the following year but no pups ever appeared. On the day on which I calculated they would be born I witnessed a strange sequence. Deneb was lying outside the gap leading to the glen. He looked relaxed. Then he suddenly leaped up, as though called, and hurried into the denning area. A moment later a wolf began to howl. I felt sure it was Musca. The voice was beautiful and so was the song, which was repeated five times, with a short interval in between each repetition. I have read that North American Native Peoples believe the distress call of a wolf is repeated four times and I have often wondered if Musca's song was a lament for still-born pups. Owing to the restrictions to which I was subject, I could do no more than wonder.

The following year Deneb was already dead and Hamal and Ara had become the breeding pair. Only one pup, Altair, survived from the litter born to Ara in 1988. This may have be been due to the bad weather that followed their birth, or to weakness as their parents were still immature.

During one spell of heavy rain, before the pups had come out into the open, Ara moved them from the den to the shelter of a big rock, part of the wall of the stone circle, and then moved them back again when the weather improved. During the move I heard their whimpers and judged there to be three or four. Only two appeared in the open, however, one of these being obviously weaker than the other and after a short time he or she ceased to appear and was never seen again.

The sole survivor, Altair, passed almost a year in comparative isolation and, when I saw him, was always with his mother or with Musca although, while both pups were alive, Rigel often took sole charge of them. Only in 1989, when he was almost a year old, did Altair venture forth more often, become more active and accompany the adults, especially Rigel, with whom I often saw him playing.

Ara was more successful in 1989 when five pups, possibly the entire litter, survived. They were very timid and hard to observe, a reaction to any potentially hostile appearance encouraged by their very timid mother. The three females were more fearful than the two males who were more influenced by their father who was tolerant of my presence. The lone pup, Regulus, born the following year, was brought up by his father as soon as he was free of the den. Hamal played with him and kept him almost constantly at his side and, to my surprise, made no effort to warn him away when I appeared.

When his parents were arbitrarily removed in the Fall of that year and Regulus was orphaned, Vega took over the care of him until, a year later, both were forced to flee the enclosure.

Musca, who had shown so much concern when leading the pack, took no part in the rearing of the last two generations, becoming more and more solitary as time passed.

MIIA

Despite Morena's heart murmur which had been diagnosed after her enforced stay in the Zoo, she was very active and in the third week in May, 1993, suddenly manifested all the signs of pregnancy and, shortly after, did not emerge from the denning area to eat. (The den was not visible from any point outside the enclosure and Morena was left completely undisturbed.) On 21 May Sandalo was seen taking meat to the denning area.

Two days later it began to rain and the rain continued, intermittently but sometimes heavily for four days. In such - unseasonal - conditions, the south heath, where the first den was located, was somewhat exposed and the pups ran a risk of contracting pneumonia. Morena, however, moved the pups to a den dug out of a steep bank just inside the eucalyptus wood which was protected from wind and rain.

When Morena began to appear, to have a break, eat and drink, she kept to herself. If she met Sandalo she greeted him submissively and then went her way. She looked well - better than before the birth - and carried herself as though proud of her achievement. She was very hungry and would not allow her brothers - including Sandalo - to touch the food until she had taken what she wanted, but a week after the pups were born she joined in play sessions and get-togethers.

During the first days all three males were very watchful and protective and checked on anyone approaching the enclosure. Apart from taking food to the den Sandalo and Manchas did "guard duty"; they could regularly be seen spaced out on the slope keeping watch.

The pups were not seen until 27 June when it transpired that there were four of them. Now that they were leaving the den Sandalo became especially protective, threatening almost all humans who came too close to the fence. Manchas and Fosco also did guard duty, while the alphas took care to teach the pups to retreat quickly as soon as a human appeared. Once, walking round the top of the enclosure in the early morning, I came upon the pups playing. I made encouraging noises and two of them started to run towards me. At once Morena dashed out of the bushes and drove them back into cover, despite the fact that both Sandalo and Morena were invariably friendly to me and, neither on this occasion nor at any other time, directed any threat at me.

The pups became daily more active in July and the adults, too, played together more often. Both Manchas and Fosco acted as "pup-sitters". There was much yelping during the pups' play sessions - the sub-hierarchy was in process of formation but all four now rarely appeared together; one of them was often absent for long periods.

The den used by Neblina and, later, by Zef was not covered over but it was fairly deep and extensive and was sited on the lip of the bank at the edge of the eucalyptus wood. It was just visible from our observation post, but we could not see into it, only watch mother and pups move in and out or lie on the lip to enjoy the view.

There was nothing unusual about the rearing of these pups until some time after they had been weaned. Then, because no close bond had been formed between Neblina and Sandalo, the former faded more and more into the background, eventually sinking to the bottom of the hierarchy and so leaving the further education of the pups to Sandalo and Fosco. This did not seem to be a problem - one good parent suffices - but it produced the unusual situation of three unhabituated pups manifesting the usual fear and wariness on the approach of humans, and the special case of Onor, who showed no more than caution and enjoyed very rapid promotion.

Due to the vasectomies performed on Sandalo and Fosco, no further births occurred in this pack. Although three males - Nimbo, Douro and Alvão - remained fertile, it was assumed that Sandalo and Fosco would prevent any subordinate mating. (And Nimbo was removed.)

MIIB

During both seasons falling within the scope of this study Clarinha and Manchas took elaborate precautions to deceive observers as to the location of the den. In the first place, and some time before confinement, they seemed undecided and gave the impression that they were choosing a site and then changing their minds. As a result of these tactics we did not know where the den was until after the pups were born and their squeaks could be heard. We expected to be able to locate when Manchas took food to his mate, but he never went straight there. Instead, he made quite complicated feints and detours and succeeded in deceiving us. (The den was eventually found to be only a hollow in the ground in the centre of an extensive and dense clump of brambles, only a few metres from the fence.)

Before the attempt to move the pups Manchas was tranquillised and while the pups were being removed - it took some time to cut through the brambles and reach the den - Clarinha, oddly calm and relaxed, joined the group of volunteers who were watching over Manchas to see that he recovered normally from the drug.

All the pups were removed - or so thought the biologist in charge of the operation. But his preconceptions prevented him from drawing the right conclusion from Clarinha's unexpected reaction to the raid. I did not know what it meant, but I did know that it bore a message and Manchas's and Clarinha's behaviour during the next few days enlightened me, for they repeated the deceptive tactics they had been using before. I therefore assumed that Clarinha had succeeded in moving one pup before the raiders had reached the den and, as I thought that Clarinha had shown remarkable aplomb, resourcefulness and intelligence and thoroughly deserved her reward, I did not mention my assumption in order to prevent further depredation by those in charge. In fact I, too, was wrong, but only numerically: Clarinha had succeeded in removing two pups, a male and a female, temporarily hiding them in a thickly wooded area at the top of the enclosure, far from the original den.

Not unexpectedly, the parents were extremely caring of these pups and it was long before they - beginning with the more adventurous male - became visible, and Clarinha, like Morena, made sure that they took cover when humans were about. However, either because I had been close to them ever since they were pups and had entered their enclosure almost every day, or because they were somehow aware of my complicity in their successful subterfuge, they made no attempt to keep the pups away from me, did not warn me away from the new denning area and even left me alone close to that area in order to attend to some supposed threat at the other end of the enclosure, thus leaving the pups at my mercy.

Strangely enough, the following year Clarinha chose to return to the original den and, this time, did not succeed in removing any of her six pups before the "raid"; but one, a female (Aura), was left behind to console her, to the great benefit of both.

Commentary

There was little difference in the form of the den between the three packs, while the location in MI was limited by the terrain to one small part of the enclosure but in MIIA and B there were several choices. In MI the same den was used repeatedly. In MIIA it was changed twice and in MIIB it was changed once but one site was used two years in succession, the change being temporary and to an emergency den.

No attempt to deceive a human onlooker as to the den-site was made by Deneb or Musca, or by Hamal or Ara in MI, but there was little and infrequent human activity in the area. In MIIA it was not evident either, perhaps because Morena did not think it necessary, her dens being well hidden, and because the very shy Neblina lacked the initiative, or the opportunity, i.e., fear prevented her from "acting" while under observation. Sandalo himself, unlike Manchas, used no evasive tactics, when taking food to the den for example, probably because, as he was in general more intelligent than Manchas, he was more confident of his capacity to cope with any threat.

Early training, too, was disparate to some extent. The pups of all the litters in MI were taught to avoid (= take cover from) humans (although the last pup, Regulus, was not taught to avoid me). Morena's pups were taught to avoid even me, with whom their mother was on the friendliest terms. Neblina's pups simply followed their mother's example with the exception of Onor, while Clarinha's pups were taught to avoid all humans except me. They were left free to approach me as they wished (which they never did).

A lone pup is physically and to some extent psychologically privileged, but is disadvantaged socially; the give-and-take of litter and juvenile pack life is very important. The side effects of the removal of pups were beneficial to the "survivors". Nursing six pups for two weeks visibly took its toll of Clarinha's physical resources; she looked thin and bare patches were visible on her coat but, within a few days of the removal, she had put on weight and her coat had recovered its normal density and lustre.

Part III

Social Life

1. Offensive and Defensive Behaviour

I do not care for the term "aggressive" with its all-too human overtones and, after observing various interactions, I have come to the conclusion that there are five main categories of offensive - and defensive - behaviour: a) agonistic, relating to the RO; b) possessive, relating to courtship and breeding; c) contraceptive, relating to breeding privilege; d) protective, relating to the pups, and e) antagonistic, relating to social tensions and/or individual relationships. Definitions, however, can be self-defeating because the relevant actions are not in practice clear-cut and the categories overlap and merge with one another; so they should not be applied too rigidly.

MI

I never witnessed any agonistic displays - dominant or submissive - between Musca and Carina or between Deneb and Neb except, in the males' case, during play sessions, when they were unrelated to rank, that is, when the alpha male would sometimes submit to the beta. The only agonistic actions I saw among these four were the chases and harassment of Carina with the apparent object of keeping her outside the RO. These chases were relaxed or in abeyance during the courtship and breeding seasons and were only resumed later in the year; even then there were periods of tolerance. This was not the case with the next generation, the members of which harassed Carina severely, having learned to harass - but not to be tolerant at the same time - from Deneb and Neb.

Until the second generation were two years old I never witnessed any agonistic displays among them. As yearlings their RO was not determined by such displays but evolved naturally and without visible conflict. Only at the start of the 1988 breeding season, as described above, did I see ritual conflicts between Hamal and Rigel and, a little later, between Ara and Vega, as the former, after successfully mating, asserted her right to the alpha female position. The only survivor of the third generation, Altair, was never seen to be involved in any such display.

Contraceptive actions were confined to the second generation. Musca never attempted to suppress the sexual freedom of her sister and Deneb, likewise, made no attempt to interfere with his brother's courtship of Carina. It is not possible to equate the harassment of Carina with contraception, in relation to the first generation, since it eased considerably at precisely these times when it would have been most indicated.

In this respect, too, the second generation were much stricter. In 1988, Hamal and Ara kept Rigel and Vega apart and the following year they repeated this action while, in addition, Hamal kept Musca temporarily isolated.

As regards possessive actions, I witnessed one dominant display by Deneb, directed against Neb, during each of the courtship seasons in 1985, 1986 and 1987. In the first year, when both males were standing close to Musca, Deneb suddenly turned on Neb with a fierce growl. The beta male immediately surrendered by lying down and raising a foreleg in the air. Deneb then desisted and their normal very friendly relations were resumed a few minutes later. In 1986 the same interaction took place under identical circumstances, but it was more prolonged and ritualistic. When Deneb turned on his brother with a growl Neb submitted by lying down and raising a foreleg. Deneb stood over him and then stood back. Neb rose and Deneb repeated his threat, with the same result. The sequence was repeated twice more, making four times in all, the same actions being precisely repeated each time. At the end all three animals, in the order Musca - Neb - Deneb, moved off together as though nothing had happened. This was a *locus classicus* of the "dominance-submission" ritual, by which Deneb firmly asserted his status and his "possession" of Musca.

In 1987, again in the same circumstances, the interaction was more curtailed. When Deneb suddenly growled - with raised tail, and testicles very prominent - Neb lowered his own tail in token of his surrender and simply moved away, but shortly after returned whereupon normal relations were resumed. Before mating took place that year Neb was dead, but the year before, during the days of mating both he and Carina were denied access to the denning area. If Neb came too near, Deneb would rush out and warn him off, giving a short, sharp bark. Neb immediately retreated. At all other times the alpha animals were not possessive and Neb was frequently in their company and often exchanged caresses with Musca.

Apart from the initial confrontation which determined Hamal's dominance, I saw no such behaviour in the second generation, but in this case the bond between the two males, Hamal and Rigel, was not nearly so strong and Rigel's relationship with Ara was very much less close than that between Neb and Musca. Rigel clearly preferred Vega's company and so there was no cause for any possessive gestures or threats.

Protective behaviour was initially confined to Deneb's protection of Musca after Carina's attack on her in August, 1985. This protection continued until Deneb's death although in the course of time it became less prolonged and intense. Otherwise protective behaviour always was exercised on behalf of the pups and principally against Carina until her death in 1989. She was not allowed to approach the pups until they were five months old and this control was at first always carried out by the males; later Ara, too intervened. The pups were also protected against humans and again it was the males who were seen to take action. If Musca sensed danger, or caught sight of an approaching human, she went to call one of the males, who would immediately assume the role of protector. The pups, if they were out in the open, would be warned by wuffs from Neb and shepherded into cover by the alpha or beta male, or by both together.

While two of Ara's pups survived the procedure was slightly different. Rigel, who was often in charge of them in the open, would warn them silently - at least I never heard him utter a sound - and they would scamper into the denning area. After one of these pups died and only Altair was left, no protective action was needed; he was so wary and timid that on his own he rushed for cover at the slightest sign of human presence and only became more confident when he was almost a year old.

The only sign of antagonistic behaviour I observed was between Deneb and Carina. They appeared to be, social roles apart, mutually antipathetic. (Neb, although he dutifully assisted his brother in chasing or harassing Carina, showed no personal hostility towards her.) Deneb never attacked or bit Carina, but he displayed hostility by posture, active signals and, on rare occasions, a sharp bark. On only one occasion did I see the positions reversed; Carina moved silently up to a reclining Deneb and nipped him in the rump. She was chased across the field for fifty metres by both males but was not otherwise punished. On another occasion, when digging up a cache, she drove both males off when they approached, but allowed Musca near. Although Carina was so much more severely treated by the second generation, especially by Hamal and Ara, this did not seem to be the result of personal antagonism.

MIIA

In this pack agonistic displays were frequent from the very beginning, especially between Morena and Clarinha to determine the female RO, Morena coming out on top while they were still pups.

On the male side Sandalo often displayed over Manchas, to establish and confirm his alpha status, but he also displayed over subordinates, especially at feeding times. He has continued to display all his life although his authority has never been disputed.

Manchas displayed over the subordinate males, Fosco and Mouro, who for many months carried on an indecisive agonistic warfare to determine their relative positions.

Agonistic displays among the females after Morena's removal occurred and resulted in a number of ranking changes but, owing to the timidity and consequent elusiveness of these females, these displays were more often heard than seen.

Owing to Sandalo's enduring pre-eminence such displays among subordinate males were limited. (Extreme agonism, resulting in omega animals, is treated separately.)

There was some antagonism, however. For a time Fosco suffered from the attentions of Sandalo and Manchas, but he survived permanent demotion partly because of his intelligent tactics and partly because he enjoyed Morena's protection: she did not allow things to go too far. Later, after both Morena and Manchas had moved elsewhere, Fosco was challenged and defeated by Nimbo but, as told above, largely through unrelated human intervention, this situation was only temporary. There was visibly an element of personal hostility in the Fosco/Nimbo relationship.

After Clarinha's removal Morena was the only female in the pack until the birth of her three daughters, and she was removed before they were old enough to be considered reproductive rivals. There was therefore no call for contraceptive offence.

During her brief ascendancy Neblina did not try to assert herself but relied on the kudos surrounding the maternal role to sustain her, and when this period passed she gradually reverted to the omega position.

Zef was more assertive and displayed against her siblings and against Neblina's Alva, but never very strongly; both sides of the SRO depended more on Sandalo than on any other.

MIIB

Manchas, a big wolf with a big appetite, sometimes loudly threatened his otherwise much-loved Clarinha when food was given them or placed in the enclosure. This action was hunger-driven and never occurred at any other time.

When Dourado and Risca were a few months old they, too, were menaced at mealtimes. Later, only Risca was often, but mildly harassed, being destined, after the growth of the privileged Aura, to be the lowest ranking member of the pack.

Commentary

Once again offensive and defensive behaviours were more complex in MI owing to the mortalities and changes of leadership. In MIIA and B the male leadership was never questioned or even tested, and the same is still the case; in MIIA the female leadership went by default.

In MI contraceptive action was undertaken by the males so long as Deneb and Neb were alive; then by Ara when she rose to the alpha position. In MIIA Morena acted alone during her brief reign; thereafter Sandalo and Fosco took over the role.

Possessive behaviour in MIIA was fiercer and more prolonged than in MI during Deneb's reign. Deneb was more tolerant than Sandalo and his feeling for Neb was much deeper than Sandalo's for Manchas. In my opinion there can be little doubt that personal feelings - likes and dislikes - in our sense of the expression, play an important part in wolf social life and therefore in the formation and stability of the SRO as well as determining at the very least the intensity of the various offensive and defensive actions and reactions.

2. *Communications*

The means of communication were - observably - fourfold: visual, vocal, olfactory and tactile.

Visual signals took three forms: active, revealing intention, interest, curiosity, affection and invitation; hierarchical, indicating rank; and passive, revealing sensation.

In the case of active signals, intention was shown by raised tail, ears and head and, if the intention was offensive, hackles. The wolves showed their curiosity by pricked ears, an intent gaze and a cautious approach. Interest was shown similarly but with less caution. Affection was signalled by a quickly wagging tail (with a small arc), ears laid back and half-opened mouth. Invitation, usually an invitation to play, was indicated by lowered head, splayed forelegs, raised rump and oblique gaze. The intention to attack, that is, to start a fight, is apparently never signalled; in such a case wolves employ a pre-emptive strike [6]. I never witnessed a fight in fourteen years of observing and I am virtually certain that none occurred in all that time.

Hierarchical signals pertain to the SRO. The wolves revealed, to one another and to me, their social rank by their stance, movement, tail position and general deportment. The tail positions were "orthodox", except that I rarely saw a tail held in the vertical position (180°). The usual dominant position of the alpha males in this pack was 30°, occasionally 90°. Deneb's tail rose to 180° only when his mate and Neb offered him their respects, something which I only witnessed after the successful breeding season in 1986 (as if they were offering their congratulations!) and, sometimes, when he smelled Musca's urinations during the courtship season. It also rose to 180° when he drove Carina from the denning area, but not when engaged in chasing her. I never saw Hamal's tail raised much above 90°, but I saw Ara's raised to 180° and waving vigorously at the same time, when asserting her dominance over Vega.

When one of the alphas wished to assert his or her dominance, he or she raised the tail while the object of their attention lowered his or hers in acknowledgement; often a fixed stare sufficed to make the point. In addition, I often witnessed acts of active submission. A subordinate would approach an alpha in a crouching position and touch his or her muzzle. Such gestures of active submission were also made by the alpha females towards their mates; the gestures are the same but the semantic content is somewhat different, yet it underlines the fact that an apparently grovelling approach by members of a wolf pack indicates affection as well as respect and supplication.

Passive submission, in response to a threat, was infrequent with the first generation; despite continual harassment I only once saw Carina submit by lying down and Neb's submissions were confined to the rare occasions already described. Later, Rigel and Vega occasionally had recourse to submissions when threatened by Hamal or Ara. Such threats were confined to the courtship and breeding season or, in Vega's case, when pups had feeding priority.

Passive signals indicate emotions, usually negative emotions such as fear, which is shown by flattened ears, a crouching position and a tail held between the legs, the object being to appear as small and inoffensive as possible. It is often followed by flight. I usually saw only the omega wolf in this situation, but all the animals, including the alphas, showed fear in the presence of strange or noisy humans. A restless pacing to and fro along a section of the fence - in this case, where space and cover were adequate and the wolves were not closely confined - seemed to indicate frustration; I only saw Neb behave in this way and only during the courtship season when he could neither mate nor enjoy his brother's company.

The eyes can be very expressive and show pain (more obviously revealed by a sharp or prolonged yelp), anxiety, curiosity and love. When the second generation were all resting in the field, I saw Ara gazing across the grass at Altair with an expression I can only describe as doting. A fixed stare, too, is not always a threat. It may express apprehension and be defensive. Once, when Musca's pups were still young, Deneb stared at me for eight minutes without moving or blinking and only relaxed when, to identify myself, I called out to him. I was too distant for clear visual recognition, but he knew my voice at once.

This leads us to vocal communication. Barks were rare and always used as a warning - "Keep away!" "Lay off!" Whines and whimpers were frequent among the adults of the first generation during get-togethers and revealed their mutual affection. I never heard the first generation of pups whimper or whine, and the second generation only on the occasion already mentioned, when they may well have been in some distress. I have wondered whether this silent behaviour, in the den and for a few weeks after leaving it, is now innate, reflecting human predation on dens. Whines and whimpers of affection were very much rarer among the wolves of the second generation, from whom also I never heard the strange sound, like a human yawn, which their elders occasionally uttered during a get-together and which, to my ear, seemed to express a profound and natural tenderness.

Growls were rare and only used to assert the ownership of a bone or piece of meat, or for possessive displays such as I have already described. "Ownership growls" seemed to be invariably respected, irrespective of rank.

Snarls were even rarer than growls and accompanied a dominance or defensive-submissive display, or sexual rejection by a female before she was receptive. Wuffs were used as warnings, both between adults and by adults to warn the pups, as described above. Clacks were heard during chases, usually chases directed against Carina, as the victim clacked her teeth together in a defensive warning.

"Yips" were short yelps (quite different from yelps of play or pain) uttered by the yearling wolves when "hunting" Carina under the direction of Deneb and Neb. Wolves are popularly believed to yip when hunting, but there is no evidence for this [6]. I suggest that yearlings yip under such circumstances because they are excited and enjoying themselves and at the same time have not yet learned that yipping while hunting wastes energy.

These are very generalised interpretations. I believe that these interpretations could be subdivided to account for subtle variations in the utterances which the normal human ear cannot detect.

I rarely heard individual howls. I have already described the occasion when Musca howled at the time of giving birth in May, 1987. On another occasion Carina howled when alone in the glen. The sound was low and mournful.

In the last year of her life I heard on several occasions Musca howl when she was quite alone in a corner of the enclosure and away from all the other members of the pack. On each of these occasions (she could not see me) she sat on her haunches, raised her muzzle to the sky and howled very softly, so softly that I, hidden quite near her, could hardly hear her gentle and very beautiful song. She was certainly not howling or, more properly, singing, in order to communicate with the other pack members or to convey information to anyone whatever and still less to call attention to herself. The reader is welcome to speculate. I shall keep my understanding of this very moving experience to myself.

I consider myself fortunate to have heard six pack howls in MI, all of them, incidentally, occurring while Deneb was still alive; thereafter I never a heard a pack howl and no lone howl other than those songs of Musca's already described.

The first pack howl took place at 3 o'clock in the afternoon, the participants being Deneb, Musca and Neb. Carina was resting nearby but did not take part. The three were playing together, when suddenly they stopped, turned to face one another, raised their muzzles and began a three-part song which, to me, seemed to be a celebration of their feeling for one another and their joy in life. It did not seem to have any practical function.

The second took place early in the morning, when Musca's pups were nine months old. All the animals, except Carina (and Neb, who was no longer there) took part. Musca remained seated, the others stood around her. They faced towards the den and howled for 30 seconds. The pups' howls were very amateurish.

Then, during the night of September 7, 1987, which I spent by the enclosure, I heard four pack howls in which all except Carina took part. Each chorus lasted 1 minute, 30 seconds and was begun by a solo voice. The first took place at 23:15, just before the pack fed. (Food had been placed in the enclosure at 17:00 hours but was not touched until 23:18.) The second chorus took place at 02:00, and appeared to have been prompted by a fire siren - it was very hot and dry and there had been many forest fires - although during daylight hours this sound had never evoked any reaction. The third chorus began at 03:00 and preceded a fire siren. The fourth occurred just before first light. In contrast to the adults whose singing was musical and mature, the yearlings, then 16 months old and therefore able to howl competently, only yipped, "laughed" and "guffawed". This supports the observation that pack "etiquette" demands that yearlings, when howling with their elders, must sound like pups [7]. The function of these choruses appeared to be to reinforce pack togetherness, especially before feeding and before dawn.

Olfactory communication is the most remote from our experience, the scent-marking of territory being one of the more easily understood forms. I never observed any sign of this among the MI wolves; they evidently regarded the fence as arbitrary and "unnatural". I never saw a wolf scent-mark this boundary. Certain tufts of grass within the area were marked and, during 1985/86 there appeared to be a "central post office" near the circle, which was marked by all the animals and was presumably where they exchanged most information; but this practice was discontinued in 1987 and never resumed.

Urinations were most frequent during the courtship period and were carefully studied. The alphas urinated with rear-leg raised (RLR) except when they merely wished to relieve themselves, when they did so squatting (SQU). Neb always used SQU until 1986, when he too, used RLR. The yearlings used SQU until September, 1987, when Hamal was seen to use RLR, perhaps a sign of his future promotion. It is generally held that RLR urination is a sign of dominance and this appeared to be so when Hamal became alpha male. That Neb used it regularly when he was beta male probably reflected his special relationship with Deneb and the latter's tolerance; it is also, in males, a sign of growing maturity and self-confidence and, when not used by the alphas, seems to signal excitement as well. Both alphas frequently scuffed the ground after urinating. The females, including these alphas, always used SQU until after the breeding season in '89, when Ara began to use RLR.

Pieces of meat, which I supplied to study their reactions (and also to give

Manchas and Clarinha   *R. Lyle*

Clarinha   *R. Lyle*

Sandalo, Manchas and Morena   *R. Lyle*

Sandalo and Morena   *R. Lyle*

Sandalo and Fosco   R. Lyle

Manchas   R. Lyle

Onor   *R. Morley*

Morena   *R. Lyle*

Sandalo   R. Morley

Fosco   R. Lyle

Sandalo and Manchas   *R. Lyle*

View over MIIA and MIIB   *R. Morley*

Deneb　　　　　　　　　　　　　　　　　　　　　　　　　*R. Lyle*

Musca　　　　　　　　　　　　　　　　　　　　　　　　　*R. Lyle*

Neb   *R. Lyle*

Hamal   *R. Lyle*

the young extra rations) were reserved, but only by Deneb, who urinated RLR on a nearby tuft of grass; he never urinated on the meat. These marks were always respected by the others, with the exception of Musca who was excluded from the proscription. In the second generation Hamal only urinated (RLR) after the meat had been collected.

On two occasions I saw Deneb mark one of two big pine trees by walking round it and rubbing his flank against the trunk. This evoked great interest in Neb and together they smelled the tree while wagging their tails in the wide arc which denotes great interest. It was just as though Deneb had written something amusing on the bark!

All the wolves occasionally rolled in muck or in anything unusual. When I offered Deneb a "liver-flavoured" dog-biscuit he showed great initial interest which quickly waned, but Neb became very excited and, when I threw it into the grass, came up - overcoming his usual shyness - smelled it and then rolled on it. Neither of them tried to eat it.

Touch is an important means of communication and, as with us, is a means of expressing positive feelings, but it was much more used by the first generation than by the second. During early get-togethers the males, Deneb and Neb, standing one on each side of Musca, would press their flanks to hers. Occasionally, during the early part of the period under review, Carina was included and all four animals expressed their mutual friendliness and togetherness by this contact. The four of the second generation only used this body contact when they were very young, rolling about and rubbing against one another. The pups of the third generation were only seen to seek body contact with their elders, particularly Hamal whom they would nuzzle and lick. Surely another instance where personal feelings play a determining role.

Muzzle contacts, which seem to be both "kisses" or friendly greetings and a source of information ("What's that you've been eating?") were frequent between Deneb and Neb and rare between Musca and Carina. They were also frequent between Deneb and Musca and not infrequent between Neb and Musca. They were not often seen between the wolves of the second generation when they were still yearlings - they occurred most often between Rigel and Vega - and became very rare when these four became adult. In fact, tactile communication was altogether much more used by the wolves of the first generation.

Neck-nuzzling (inhibited biting) often occurred between Deneb and Neb but appeared to have no RO significance; it was just affectionate play. It was rare between these two and the younger wolves, being usually a brief dominant display which evoked a submissive display in response.

Mountings occurred between Deneb and Neb but, again, had no RO significance since the beta usually mounted the alpha! They were also seen during the night I spent by the enclosure among the yearlings during a juvenile get-together (the adults took no part) again without any RO significance, for all four animals took part in the ceremony and changed roles.

Deneb and Musca mutually indulged in licking of the belly and inguinal regions on many occasions; so did Deneb and Neb but much less often. The alphas practised it on the pups, much less frequently as they grew older. I also saw it among the pups themselves, but it later ceased and I never observed it among the members of the second generation after they grew up.

Mouth contact - soliciting for food - was used by the pups to persuade the alpha male to regurgitate for them and, more rarely, from the beta male; but Vega, as well as Rigel, was sometimes solicited. It was also used by the yearlings to obtain food from Deneb until his death, by which time they were already eighteen months old. For obvious reasons, captive wolves are more retarded than those in the wild! Altair, too, when a yearling, solicited from Hamal until the birth of the fourth generation. Musca and Ara also used this soliciting approach to their respective mates on many occasions, but this was less a request for food than a gesture of affectionate submission.

Deneb and Neb frequently used to wrestle, standing on their hindlegs, and once only I saw Neb and Carina wrestle together. Musca and Carina never indulged in this form of contact; the second generation did so occasionally as yearlings. Until the birth of the fourth generation Altair and Rigel were sometimes seen to indulge in this form of play.

Although all the wolves groomed themselves, I never saw one animal groom another.

Regular get-togethers involved every kind of communication, visual, vocal, olfactory and tactile, but these became much more casual among the wolves of the second generation and the lone wolf of the third.

Lastly, touch is involved in resting. Pups rest in close contact, for security and, when appropriate, warmth, but as they grow older they separate and each one occupies his or her "personal space", which is greatly respected. Adults usually rest some way apart, but Deneb and Neb often rested in very close proximity, a sign of their mutual devotion.

MIIA

The more general remarks in MI above refer equally to MIIA and B because we are dealing with a language or, more accurately, a common communications system.

The main difference between this pack and MI concerns howling, partly because I had far more opportunities to hear them but also because more than one enclosure was involved and therefore there was a need for extra-mural communication. But spontaneous and seemingly non-functional group howls were frequent, especially at night, lasting from a few minutes to a half hour and then repeated.

For a long time after Morena's removal she would howl with the obvious purpose of eliciting a response from Sandalo and, for weeks, he duly obliged, no doubt feeling the separation as much as she did. Very often Fosco also responded. But Sandalo's responses became fewer and weaker after Morena's rejection.

Morena has a particularly beautiful mezzo-soprano voice, piercing but in no way shrill and with a timbre strikingly like that of the Indian bamboo flute. When I first heard a recording of Hariprasad Chaurasia playing the slow introductory alap of Rag Lalit on a bamboo flute I was at once reminded of Morena, not only because of the likeness between the two timbres but, even more remarkably (and more generally) because of the similarity between the intervals of the Rag Lalit and those of the scale used by wolves when howling. It is also worth noting, in passing, that the Rag Lalit is to be performed at dawn, when wolves, too, are accustomed to perform. It was not possible to hear Morena during these antiphons with her ex-mate without oneself feeling the longing and, especially in the earlier stage of these exchanges, the distress which she suffered. Among her habitual respondents it was interesting to note that Fosco had a deeper voice than that of his chief.

During the first two years of their stay in C3 I would often call them down from their refuges by howling myself and they rarely failed to hurry down to greet me. At all times it has almost always been possible for a human to initiate a group howl, although the one they responded too most readily and enthusiastically was that of Luis Miguel Moreira who had rescued them from their abandoned den and hand-reared them for their first few weeks of life.

After the first escape in March 1992 the five escapers rushed out of cover and were easily recaptured in response to a howl. This of course is an example of one of the main known functions of the howl: to call the members of the pack together. But I am in no doubt that, just as we can use our voices for several purposes from prayer to ordering a meal or making a speech, so wolves, too, can use their voices to express their feelings as well as to send messages, give orders, or pass on information.

Barks, wuffs, yelps, whines and growls in this pack were "orthodox". The meaning - one meaning! - and effectiveness of the whine as a means of appeasement was clearly revealed when a young biologist entered the enclosure and was unexpectedly threatened by Sandalo who placed his forepaws on the man's shoulders and growled menacingly. The man turned pale but kept his head and whimpered like a pup. Sandalo immediately relaxed, jumped aside and wandered off. On the other hand an older biologist, who should have known better, but whose vanity required him always to be the dominant animal, had the tables turned on him one fine day and thereafter was denied access to the enclosure.

Each of these sounds has more than one meaning; there are subtle nuances, and their semantic content is changed or augmented when they are used in the various possible combinations. Sandalo would sometimes greet me by placing his forepaws on my shoulders - not a submissive action - and then whimper or whine like a pup, clearly expressing affection. In the first instance he was at least my equal; in the second, once more the pup acknowledging his foster-father.

Growls varied in intensity according to the context and the wolf, or human, involved. When, tactlessly, I entered C3 and approached Morena during oestrus, Sandalo, standing nearby, growled softly to warn me. I understood and turned away. He came up and took my right arm, very gently, in his jaws and escorted me to the gate where he let me go. Two days later, oestrus being over, he made no protest when I went to greet Morena.

Barks may serve to warn another wolf away - a wuff is to warn another of an external threat - or it may combine a warning with the expression of shocked surprise or pain, as when a wolf touches an electric fence. This happened in C3 very soon after the electric fence was installed. But wolves learn quickly and they very rarely made this mistake after the first day.

With this pack it was much easier to observe reactions to humans as well as to other wolves. Wolves are very quick to divine the character of any human approaching their territory although they sometimes makes mistakes, assuming that a man carrying a pick or a shovel is hostile when he is merely going about his business quite unconnected with the animals. Under normal circumstances they threaten some humans, run away from others (a common reaction) and greet a few with obvious pleasure. Weaknesses which we overlook or are not aware of are apparent to them for they can read "body-language" much better than most of us - it is after all, the basis of their communications system! Many humans, especially Englishmen, suffer from repressed aggression and the unconscious muscular and comportmental expression of this is at once apparent to a wolf who reads it as a threat and will usually run away. (Sandalo, exceptionally, usually took up a threat stance: hackles raised, tail up, teeth exposed.)

I had a long, friendly relationship with Sandalo and this involved learning his "body language" and becoming fully aware of and learning to use my own. (I spoke to him and to all the wolves, most of the time I was with them, chatting in a friendly way to convey my feelings and intentions through the sound of my voice: loving words are automatically accompanied by loving sounds!) He had a charming habit of saying "hello" by very briefly flicking his ears back when he recognised me. All wolves and, indeed, all canids do this, but it was particularly noticeable in his case.

He would also show jealousy. If Fosco tried to come close and greet me, Sandalo would growl and turn on his brother, biting his neck and forcing him to keep his distance.

The boundary was not scent-marked; here, too, the boundary - the fence - was imposed, not chosen. Urinations were used on selected clumps within the area and were, of course, more frequent during courtship. Urinations to reserve lumps of meat occurred, but not often. Rolling on food, especially if it was "going off", was a regular phenomenon, but it was normally reserved for "wild" food - goat, donkey - not butcher's meat; a clear indication of their preference. The pups solicited food from all the adults but they were weaned from this practice before they were a year old.

In this pack grooming was frequent; the alphas in particular, often groomed the younger wolves.

MIIB

For the first year the alphas were alone in the enclosure. They were almost always together, a tactile togetherness which was intensified after Clarinha gave birth to her first litter in 1995.

A different kind of communication - hostile in this case - was often seen between the two alphas of the adjacent packs, C4 and C3. Sandalo and Manchas tore silently up and down the parallel strip of fencing - about 100m - or confronted each other through the wire, tails high, hackles raised, eyes stern, each making himself as large and threatening as possible. That Manchas had, under Sandalo, been a much harassed omega wolf now meant nothing. The possession of a territory changed everything.

Sandalo was frequently accompanied in this exercise by Fosco and by Onor. Clarinha followed Manchas up and down the fence but without much enthusiasm. On the other hand Dourado joined his father as soon as he was old enough to do so.

Manchas was somewhat rough with his pups but Clarinha was very gentle, grooming them and paying much attention first to Dourado and then to Aura.

The content of a bark was vividly shown by Manchas when he touched the electric fence. He must have communicated pain because Clarinha, who was not far away, came running to him and, in an obviously concerned way, touched his muzzle. She so clearly said: "What is it, my love? Are you alright?"

Commentary

Not surprisingly, since we are dealing with a common system, the differences between these packs are minimal and idiosyncratic. The main difference - and this is incidental - involves reactions to or communications with humans. In MI the wolves were not habituated and no one socialised with them: they ran into cover and hid while the humans were in the vicinity - or panicked if they entered the enclosure. Most of them reacted in like manner to me although I was a quiet, slow-moving and familiar presence. Only Deneb became, first tolerant and then friendly and trusting. I did, however, establish a tenuous contact with Vega, despite her timidity, born, in part, of her necessity.

I frequently took food to the wolves and this was usually seized upon by Deneb and, later, by Hamal and Ara. Vega, who often had to go hungry, carefully observed my visits and my movements - she knew very well what I was about. I therefore took to leaving some meat for the alphas to collect and then, as unobtrusively as possible, moved to another part of the enclosure to deposit what was left. Vega, who watched me carefully from cover, would then dash out and seize her prey. This became a regular practice, made possible by an exchange of simple signals. It was not always successful since the alphas were also very observant and the operation became a quite complex exchange of tactical moves and feints.

Such mutual cooperation was also possible with the omega wolves in C3 - it was never possible with Carina, she was too frightened - but in this case communication was much easier because they had been hand-raised and therefore, in those circumstances, looked upon familiar humans as their friends and saviours. With the first generation in C3 and in C4, and with the hand-raised pups, it was also possible to communicate visually and by touch.

In a word the differences are related to upbringing and opportunity and need no elaboration. Basic "wolfish", which is as much as most of us can learn, is a constant. Subliminal communication is another matter which, perhaps fortunately, lies outside our present terms of reference since it, too, is common to the species irrespective of local circumstances although graduated according to individual capacity and development.

3. Education

Wolves learn and/or are taught the facts of life in four ways: by example; by experience; by example and experience; and by instruction. These ways will be illustrated by examples as we study the learning behaviour of these packs.

In captivity learning is mostly confined to the first year and is carried out in play sessions. These occurred frequently between Deneb and Neb and during their second winter were almost daily events. Their frequency diminished as time passed but they still occurred as late as 1987. In them they learned to understand each other and to establish their social roles without any serious conflict.

When the second generation were pups I often witnessed play sessions. At first these were usually supervised by Deneb and Neb. They involved chases in which the three "senior" pups chased Hamal, who invariably ended up by lying down with his legs in the air, an act of submission which ended the session. This was interesting in view of Hamal's eventual ascendance. In these sessions they learned to be mutually tolerant and to exercise restraint; in a word, they learned to live together - an example of learning by experience. Their elders discouraged a too aggressive approach and I have seen Deneb intervene to stop it. He did so when Ara later replaced Hamal as the victim. On one occasion when things got too hot for her, he promptly intervened, tail level, to see she came to no harm.

"Avoidance learning" was also part of the curriculum. The pups were taught to be wary of humans as soon as they were out of the den; an example of learning by instruction. When Reserve personnel entered the enclosure in March, 1987, to remove Neb, all four pups (then 10 months old) immediately took refuge in the glen and were not seen again until long after the men had departed.

Altair, the "only pup" of the third generation, hardly needed this form of instruction; he showed intense wariness of humans, including myself, from the beginning. By contrast, the pups of the fourth generation were much less afraid of me, though not of other humans. This was probably due to Hamal's example: he trusted me more, so far as pups were concerned, than Deneb did. Consequently, they were not taught to scatter when I appeared, but only on the appearance of a stranger; they were evidently taught - by example - to discriminate.

In captivity there is no opportunity to hunt as a pack, the most important part, after pup-rearing, of wolf life. In some captive conditions (v.infra) it is possible to hunt small mammals, but this was not so in MI. But that neither the instinct nor the ability to hunt atrophies in captivity was shown when a covey of partridges landed in the enclosure. They were stalked by Deneb and Neb and the beta male chased and caught one of them just as they were taking off in alarm. Carina rushed up and tried to take the bird from him - she was probably very hungry - but Deneb intervened and drove her off. Neb then shared the remains of the bird with his brother.

After Neb's death the yearlings joined Deneb in brief chases of Carina. Deneb led the "attack" and the yearlings manoeuvred into position to prevent her escape. They were learning the technique of co-operative hunting, this time, learning by example. In the wild young wolves learn to hunt large prey by watching their elders. At that time, under Deneb, the attacks were never pressed home; only when Hamal had taken over was Carina bitten and actual wounds inflicted. This lesson had been learned too well - but such are the pains of captivity if humans do not intervene.

MIIA

I have already described how Morena thoroughly imbued the pups of her litter with fear of humans, including myself, at a very early age - an example of avoidance learning by instruction. In the case of Neblina's pups, these seemed to have learned the same lesson by the example of their mother. In Zef's case there was no evidence that she taught them to fear humans, and in the event, they showed less fear than Neblina's pups, perhaps because Zef is herself less afraid than Neblina. (This may be by example, but I am inclined to think it an example of subliminal communication.)

The exception is the case of Onor, who was not taught to flee humans, doubtless because he was Sandalo's favourite and protégé - an example of instruction exploiting innate disposition.

Play sessions, and their results, differed little in this pack from those in MI.

Small prey could not enter this enclosure and so there was no actual hunting. As in MI chasing omega wolves taught them the technique and tactics.

One of Zef's pups provided a delightful example of learning by example before the meaning of the lesson had been discovered by experience. The pup carefully carried a piece of meat onto the slope and buried it in the orthodox manner under a shrub. Pleased with himself, he trotted off, only to return ten minutes later, to dig it up again.

MIIB

In this case, too, I have already described how Manchas and Clarinha did not teach their pups to avoid me. They nevertheless showed fear, but much less than they would have done had they been taught to take to flight.

This pack was much smaller than the other two and play sessions more often included the adults, especially Clarinha. otherwise ways and results were the same.

An electric fence provided an opportunity to learn - very rapidly and lastingly - from experience. I never saw any sign that the pups were taught to avoid it - but it doesn't move, a very significant qualification.

This enclosure (C4) was built after C3 and drainage is provided by tubes let into the wall instead of the upended bricks that were used for C3. As a result, small prey, including rabbits, can enter - and leave - the enclosure. They therefore can be, and are sometimes, hunted, with limited success as the habitat favours the prey. Instinct rather than instruction is involved in this case, as hunting small prey is an individual rather than a pack occupation.

Commentary

The subject - education - and our material provokes questions about lupine (and mammalian) intelligence. No great intelligence is needed to watch and then imitate the actions of an adult, but when an adult teaches pups to do, or not to do, this or that, how are we to understand this except as a conscious decision? The variations only tend to support this interpretation. Deneb in MI, Morena in MIIA, do not discriminate between one human and another; they teach unqualified avoidance; but Hamal in MI and, even more, Clarinha and Manchas in MIIB discriminate: some of us are more dangerous than others!

Such discrimination may not be conscious, however. I once visited a she-wolf - I named her Mira - held in very restricted captivity by the Forestry Services at Lamego, in central Portugal. She proved to be one of the most immediately affectionate animals I have ever known, but I was told that she was not so with all her visitors. At the first sight of some she would retreat, tail down, and crouch fearfully in the farthest corner of her small yard. This, it seems to me, was instinctive, a reaction based, perhaps, on her interpretation of the visitor's body language, or simply "received" as a result of a subliminal assessment of the visitor's real nature.

On many occasions I have been surprised by a wolf's inability to solve what seemed to me a very simple problem. At other times I have been equally surprised by the evidence of great intelligence. In the cases we are considering, Clarinha's pup-tuition, in so far as it was discriminating, seems to be more intelligent than Morena's comprehensive proscription. But, in the long run, in the context of species survival, probably Morena's and Deneb's behaviour was the wiser. This may explain why, when they were members of the same pack, Morena was the alpha female and Clarinha the omega animal.

When considering the complex question of "intelligence", however, we should always bear in mind Krishnamurti's profound saying: "Intelligence has nothing to do with thought". This moment of illumination casts a bright light on so much that is otherwise dubious or obscure.

4. Food for Thought

MI

Food, in the form of a large hunk of frozen meat, was dumped inside this enclosure, near the gate, twice a week. As it was almost always frozen hard, no approach to it was made for at least two hours - they soon learned how long it took to unfreeze! - but, occasionally, Deneb or Neb, or both together, would briefly verify its condition, smell the gate and the tracks of the man or men and then retire to the far side of the enclosure.

When the time came Neb was often the first to approach. He was usually accompanied by his brother. The feeding order of the first generation was usually Neb - Deneb - Musca and, lastly, Carina. Deneb and Neb often fed together and were joined by Musca when she was unaware of my presence. Only Neb was heard, rarely, to growl over food. Sometimes the food was consumed where it had been left; at other times it was dragged further down the slope or even to the edge of the glen. Usually all the food was utilised on the same day, but at times some was left for a day or more. This probably reflected the quality of the food rather than the degree of hunger, for when I took food it was always eaten immediately under all circumstances. But appetite was also affected by weather conditions since much less energy was expended in play, chases, etc., when the weather was hot.

Rules about feeding became stricter during the females' pregnancies and after the birth of pups. I have already described Deneb's feeding of Musca during her pregnancy in May, 1986. At this time, too, Deneb ate much more than usual - insisting as well on his priority - consuming large quantities at a sitting, presumably to regurgitate much of it later in the den for his pregnant mate. He was also thrifty; when Musca left a piece of meat in the grass, Deneb cached it. Musca was also seen to cache meat given to her by Deneb and to dig up and consume meat previously cached by him. Hamal, in his turn, was equally careful of Ara and, instead of amicably sharing as he would do at other times of the year, insisted, forcibly if necessary, on his right to be first served.

After Musca's pups were born the males dragged the meat down to the circle and left it where Musca had easy access to it. At this time, too, I began to take small quantities (2kg) of stewing beef to see what Deneb would do with it. This experiment began when the pups were being weaned; they were still suckling but beginning to eat regurgitated meat at five weeks of age. At first Deneb took the meat straight to the den. Neb also sometimes did this. Then, when the pups began to move about outside the denning area, they were sometimes fed in the open but were always shepherded away to a safe distance from me - though not out of sight - before being fed. Sometimes the pups solicited their father for food, but more often he regurgitated for them without being prompted. Deneb usually ate the meat before feeding his pups, but sometimes he took a piece in his mouth and carried it straight to the den, presumably to give to his mate. During Musca's second, unsuccessful pregnancy, he was often intercepted on his way to the den by the yearlings. He adopted various tactics in an attempt to avoid them, but they were usually successful in obtaining something to eat.

When his turn to be the caring father came round, Hamal was much less indulgent and made sure that every piece he collected was fed to the pups or to his mate. Nevertheless, after the birth of Ara's first litter in 1988, Hamal allowed Rigel to take food to the den. I never saw these pups fed in the open, nor did I ever see the surviving pup, Altair, fed at any time although I did hear food being regurgitated for him. After the birth of Ara's second litter in May, 1989, however, Hamal alone took food to the den for the first ten days. Then, during the next two weeks, he and Ara collected it together, driving away any other pack member who tried to collect it. Even Rigel was chased away and forced to submit. Hamal and Ara worked under pressure, collecting the food as quickly as possible, with raised tails and, if another were near, with raised hackles. At the same time Ara would solicit vigorously from Hamal, licking his mouth as she ran alongside him. She appeared to be very hungry.

When the pups were fully weaned, however, vigilance was relaxed and Rigel and Vega also collected meat together with Hamal, whose level of tolerance varied. As the pups often solicited from Rigel and Vega, usually without success, these two presumably also gave them something, although they were not seen to do so. In Vega's case, she was almost certainly concerned to feed herself as, being the subordinate female, she was relegated to the end of the food queue and was correspondingly hungry.

When Musca's pups had grown and fed themselves from the main supply, Deneb and Neb, as before, usually approached first. After an interval they were followed by the young wolves, Rigel often being the first. The feeding order was then Neb - Deneb - Rigel - Vega. Musca and Ara fed later when the pack was under observation. Carina, as before, fed last.

When food was left and before it had become warm enough to eat, Carina was often subjected to a chase or to harassment, possibly to remind her that she was last in the order of preference and, in fact, if she tried to approach the meat before it was her turn, she was usually - though not always - chased away. Later, when Hamal and Ara took over the leadership, she was always chased away. The feeding order at that time sometimes varied. For example, it might be Neb - Rigel - Deneb - Vega. In other words, there was no apparent rivalry;

the young deferred to their elders out of respect but were not forced to do so. Again, this changed to some extent when the second generation took over; a more rigorous system operated and the alphas were much more concerned to insist on their rights.

When Deneb took food supplied by me to the den during the third, unsuccessful season, he was invariably intercepted by the yearlings who solicited him relentlessly for food and, very often, he gave way and fed them. He tried various ways of avoiding their attentions with only intermittent success; one growl would have sufficed to deter them but he evidently could not resist their demands. The second generation in fact seemed somewhat retarded, perhaps because first, they had had no contact with humans - some degree of habituation at an early age increases initiative - and, secondly, because no pups survived in 1987; the presence of pups would have provided both an interest and an occupation and would have accelerated their maturation. These factors may also explain a certain apathy in their behaviour - until they themselves became protectors of pups - when contrasted with that of their elders.

MIIA

This pack was fed three times a week and the food, of a much better quality than that supplied to MI, was not dumped inside the gate but distributed in various ways. Also it was never given frozen and so could be consumed at once. It was not left in one place but was scattered around and, sometimes, in order to stimulate the wolves' interest, it was distributed in different parts of the enclosure. Some of the wolves, always from the senior ranks, were fed by hand, not only to cement social contacts, but because it gave the staff the chance of a close-up look at the animals.

Before Morena's removal she and Sandalo were always the first members to approach the food. Manchas, when beta male, sometimes kept them company but at others was threatened and had to wait his turn. None of the subordinates was allowed to approach until the alphas had had their fill.

The wolves had no trouble with hunks of beef or with chickens which were eaten bones and all and crunched up in a very short time. When the carcass of a cow which had died was placed inside, the wolves, who at that time were still yearlings, were not able to penetrate the hide and one of the staff had to open it for them. They were also fed goats and sheep (previously killed) preferring this meat to beef. In general, the wilder the meat the better they liked it, but they showed a distinct preference for donkey-meat over any other, domestic or wild.

There was not much conflict at feeding time because the subordinate wolves clearly "knew their place" and did not approach until the coast was clear, a behaviour which may well occur more in captivity than in the wild where the pressure of hunger is usually greater. Such conflict as there was - growls and brief, abortive attacks - occurred between the seniors.

Sandalo, Morena, Fosco and, later, Onor, took food from my hand. Fosco could only do this if Sandalo was otherwise occupied and did not intervene. Sandalo himself took it from me with great delicacy. When once, by mistake, his teeth met on my hand, he released it immediately.

The feeding of the pups was "orthodox". At first Sandalo took food to the den. Then he, Morena, Manchas and Fosco all took part. When able to feed themselves Morena's pups approached the feeding area separately, carefully and at intervals, all the time watching their elders' movements. Nimbo was always ahead of his sisters. Neblina's pups followed the same pattern, although Neblina herself did not enjoy an alpha's privileges, and there was the already mentioned exception - Onor - who, when still very much a pup, came down with his father and fed with him, enjoying precedence over the beta, Fosco.

MIIB

Manchas, a big wolf, ate as much as he could seize and, when he could not immediately eat it, conceal. He, too, took from my hand but, unlike his brother, Sandalo, snatched the meat greedily. He was also more ruthless with his mate, growling at Clarinha, serving himself first, and only thinking of her during the last days of pregnancy and after the pups were born. Here, too, the pups were taught to await their turn; Manchas drove them away if they approached while he was eating, but he was more tolerant of Dourado than of Risca. Gastronomically these wolves showed the same preferences as those of MIIA.

Commentary

The differences are not so much specific as individualistic. Deneb and Sandalo, Neb and Manchas, were different personalities. Deneb allowed Neb priority; Sandalo denied it to Manchas. Deneb was more solicitous for Musca's welfare than was Sandalo for Morena's, let alone Neblina's. Manchas, although in other respects more devoted to Clarinha than was Sandalo even to Morena and as much so as Deneb was to Musca, was more selfish than either where food was concerned.

MI's pups, especially of the first generation, were allowed more freedom than those of either of the other two packs, the result, I am sure, of Deneb's tolerant and self-confident disposition.

Other points that should be taken into account are 1) the wolves of MI had less to eat than those of the other two packs; 2) the food in MIIA and B was more varied and of much better quality; 3) it was supplied three times a week in a readily accessible condition, and 4) the frequent presence of human helpers or observers affected the behaviour of the subordinate wolves in MIIA and B.

Omega wolves in captivity feed last of all and often survive on scraps left here and there by the others. They tend to emerge from hiding during the hours when the rest are enjoying a siesta, usually during the afternoon after the feeding day. They may show considerable ingenuity in their struggle for survival. I once saw Vega emerge from cover and approach the meat in MI while it was still frozen and therefore ignored by the others. She bit off a large hunk and carried it back to her refuge in the heather to eat it, hopefully, undiscovered, when time had made it edible. Her slinking, surreptitious approach to the meat, making full use of the available cover, and her timing, showed clearly that she had made a correct appreciation of the situation, had planned the operation based on her own observations, and had carried it out successfully with great skill. Not a bad effort.

5. The Omega Wolf

MI

Carina was already marginalised when observation began and she was eighteen months old but, as reported, harassment remained mild, more of a game or exercise than a persecution until, after Deneb's death, Hamal became leader and harassment escalated. Her ostracism does not seem to have been related to breeding privilege since the alpha female, Musca, never joined in any action against her.

After Carina was found dead there followed an interval of nine months before Vega, in her turn, was marginalised, although she was never persecuted as severely as Carina had been. Her case differs from Carina's in three respects: she was not, initially, marginalised, having started off as a full pack member; her demotion was initiated and led by the alpha female, Ara, and was therefore related to breeding (she did not suffer during Musca's 18-month interregnum); and she was more aware than Carina who gave an impression of hopeless resignation.

MIIA

Clarinha's subordination and eventual ostracism was clearly related to breeding privilege since it was begun and maintained by Morena, the alpha female.

Her successor in this unenviable situation, Mouro, seems to have suffered because he was not content to "keep his place" but sought to rise in the hierarchy. There was in fact no female successor to Clarinha since, after her removal, Morena was the only female until the birth of her pups.

Manchas, who was next, was demoted from the beta position for reasons that remain obscure.

Nimbo, of the second generation, made the mistake of failing to pay homage to his chief when Sandalo returned after being vasectomised.

All these wolves were duly removed and subsequently flourished, with the exception of Mouro, who escaped and is believed to have been shot by a hunter.

At this writing Neblina is the omega animal but she is not completely isolated and her condition is not so bad as to demand removal.

MIIB

Manchas and Clarinha, the alpha pair, were both omegas who were removed from MIIA. Risca is the subordinate wolf but is not marginalised. There is not yet, and has never been, an omega wolf in this pack.

Commentary

Although this phenomenon is "natural" in the wild, it is to the human observer distressing and in captivity, which is unnatural, it can be very distressing, especially if the observer cannot exercise any control over the situation, as was the case with two of my subjects. With the others I was able to intervene and bring about their removal.

In the wild an omega wolf can leave the pack, to seek for his or her own territory and, eventually, to mate. In captivity this is impossible and the suffering is not only much more severe but is the direct result of human action - captivity. It therefore rests with the humans responsible to bring relief to the animal concerned which requires, as a corollary, that any captive facility should have spare accommodation to meet such an emergency.

As to the causes of this social phenomenon, some are evident while others are obscure. Pack tensions tend to erupt during the late autumn when, in the wild, most dispersals take place, presumably because the innate fear of food shortages in winter impels the leaders to reduce the size of the pack, and again, early in the year when the onset of the courtship/breeding season requires a strictly ordered hierarchy and an undisputed breeding prerogative. In addition, and at other times, wolves seek to improve their positions in the SRO when they may meet with opposition which escalates into the demotion or even expulsion of one or other of the protagonists.

There is also the possibility that a wolf is excluded because of some physical or psychological disability which could prove a handicap to the pack. I have not seen anything, however, to support this hypothesis; rather the contrary as we shall see.

There are parallels for this phenomenon, not only, as we might suppose, with the ways of the North American Native Peoples, but also with our own social norms. Among groups who live by hunting, aberrant or egoistic behaviour cannot be tolerated because it threatens the group's survival; it is therefore subject to various degrees of threat or discipline, culminating, as the last resort, in expulsion.

In our case the situation is of course more complex. Behaviour is judged by reference to a legal system and, if judged guilty, is punishable according to established laws, imprisonment being the partial equivalent to ostracism, while, in some societies e.g. the ex-USSR - the precise equivalent of exile has been used.

Ostracism in small groups, however, may occur without the commission of any "crime" which might call for punishment. In this case it is both more subtle and closer to the same phenomenon in the wolf pack. With us it is usually found among the young or among adults who are emotionally immature. Anyone who has attended school knows the phenomenon and may have suffered from it. In my experience it is always provoked by some departure from what is considered "normal" by the group in question. This may be concerned with dress, speech, manners, interests or whatever; evidently by its very deviation it calls in question the ethos of the group and therefore undermines its probably vulnerable sense of security, posing a threat which must be corrected or eliminated.

In the purely animal world "fitness" may play an even more determining role than it does with us. But "fitness" is not easily defined. Of the two females, Morena and Clarinha, the first was preferred by the undisputed alpha male and easily established her ascendancy over her sister, although she was from the start the more vulnerable of the two, having a congenital defect - a heart murmur - and testing positive and periodically exhibiting symptoms of leishmaniasis, while Clarinha has always enjoyed excellent health and is free of all physical or neurological defects. The last example among the females, Carina, larger and seemingly fitter than her sister, the alpha female, was marginalised throughout her largely unhappy life. Neb, too, larger and more powerful than Deneb, never aspired to be more than the beta to his brother's alpha. The case of Manchas is comparable. The largest and heaviest wolf in his pack, he is very powerful and has a clean bill of health, while his dominant brother has tested positive for leishmaniasis, although he has never exhibited visible symptoms of that dread disease. The "survival of the fittest" does not, apparently, refer only to physical fitness but to an overall fitness in which the physical may not predominate.

One thing stands out from consideration of this phenomenon and applies to animal and human alike.

Ostracism causes great distress, is so painful and undesired that the subjects, especially if they are wolves, will endure painful and repeated harassment rather than suffer separation from their kin. This horror of involuntary isolation is of course quite different from the case of the wolf who goes off to spend some time alone, or the human who seeks periods of solitude. It is painful because we - the "we" includes both species - are essentially social beings, but it is also painful, even insupportable, because our individuality and separateness is in reality an illusion:

The One remains, the many change and pass...

6. Territory

The alphas of this pack never scent-marked the boundary of their enclosure; they therefore, as I have noted, regarded the fence as arbitrary. On the other hand they distinguished clearly between an approach outside the fence and entry into it. They seemed to know that it limited their freedom of movement but did not seem to know that it also limited that of outsiders - unless they were sufficiently aware to realise that humans can effect entry and animals cannot, for they showed fear of a human approach but either curiosity or complete indifference to the approach of fallow deer, horses, or wild boar.

Flight distance was much greater by day than by night and entry into the area usually caused panic - even Deneb was disturbed and his pack mates were panic-stricken - unless the entry involved only one or two people and these moved slowly and kept quiet. When I entered, alone, to search for Deneb's remains, there was no panic, but the wolves moved quietly away and hid themselves in the heather. On that occasion I was fascinated to discover that the constant use and movement of the wolves had made the glen like a village, with a "main street" running down the middle and with "side-streets" running off at right angles on each side through the undergrowth. It left a real impression of communal life.

The pack members' use of the area as a whole varied from generation to generation. In Deneb's time the area in front of the twin pines (B4) was a favourite resting-place and also the "observation post": it commands a good view of the approaches. But this site did not become traditional; it was hardly ever used by the second and third generations who preferred the east slope on the other side of the valley (Cl and C2). Again, the utilisation of space varied from year to year and, at much shorter intervals, according to weather conditions. While the pines area was the observation post the males rested there, while the females often preferred the cover of the glen, and get-togethers were held in the south heath. Later, less use was made of the observation area and get-togethers were moved to the eastern quadrant, a change which was maintained thereafter. In hot weather the wolves naturally sought the most shaded areas. They were not affected by rain but sought shelter from high winds, which also made them nervous as they could not hear so well. Carina was often restricted to a particular area; to the south heath in 1985, to the north heath in 1986 and to the west and north heaths in 1987, but there were periods when she moved around more freely.

Chases revealed that all, but especially Deneb, possessed cognitive maps of the area, or, in plain English, that they carried a clear and detailed picture of their territory in their minds. Deneb made accurate use of short-cuts through cover, when his "prey" was invisible, in order to intercept her. He showed a precise awareness of time and distance. He "invented" this tactic, which was later copied by Neb.

The space available (1 hectare) was, to judge by their behaviour, adequate for the four wolves of the first generation and for them and their pups in 1986. It still seemed adequate for the seven surviving wolves in the Winter of 1987 and 1988. Stress was still not apparent then when there were six adults and five pups in the enclosure. Numbers were held down by the deaths of Deneb, Neb and Carina and by the loss of some pups at or soon after birth. But space cannot be judged only in terms of square metres or of suitable habitat; social and individual factors can be decisive.

MIIA

The senior wolves did not scent-mark the boundary, but they did patrol it, paying most attention to the sides from which humans approached.

The wolves use of the area was fairly consistent, chiefly, I think, because this was determined by the nature of the terrain. There is only one extensive open space - it has shrubs and bushes scattered about - and this was and is used by all but the most subordinate for get-togethers, play sessions and siestas. It is also used as the main observation area. During Morena's lying-in and after the birth of her pups, for example, Sandalo and Manchas and Fosco mounted guard on this slope. A much smaller grassy patch, near the entrance enclosure was also used for resting. Of course, much observation by the wolves is carried out from concealed positions in the heaths or in the wood from which they can see and be forewarned without being seen. Another favourite observation post and resting place was located at the top of the highway where a ridge offered a good view from it and concealment in the hollow behind it. It became popular after the pups emerged from the den, when the slope was considered too exposed and too near human activity for their safety.

The vegetation was in general fairly dense and it became denser as time passed. Great use was made of it, for chases, games and concealment and it was honeycombed with tracks.

The omega wolves all ended up near the top fence in hollows under the brambles. So long as they stayed in them they were relatively safe even against a combined onslaught. Only when they left, to eat or drink, were they more or less defenceless and suffered accordingly.

The greatest number of wolves existing in this enclosure at any one time was ten (in the first half of 1996). The space (13,000m²) seemed adequate.

As in this case there were other wolves in other enclosures, there was more consciousness of occupancy and the wolves visibly reacted to what they interpreted as a threat to their homeland.

MIIB

Although the space available was the same as in MIIA, it was more thoroughly covered with woodland and heath and there was no large open space available. Such open space as there is - a long, grassy strip, formerly a track -was high up and out of sight of the humans' observation post. It was much used by adults and pups for play sessions because it lay between the two denning areas, but Manchas and Clarinha liked to rest in the heath above the entrance enclosure because it gave them a good view of the human approaches and also of their rivals in MIIA.

Use of the area was remarkably consistent and varied little as time passed. The denning area was only briefly changed after the pups removal in 1995. Clarinha used it again in 1996. Near to it, a small open space was much used as a dining area. The wolves would bring their food to this spot and eat it there. It was and is still, quiet and secluded. This spot, and the den, is connected to the grassy track by long tunnels through the dense heather which rise steeply up the eastern side of the enclosure.

The subordinate female, Risca, was not restricted in her movements, except at feeding times, but she tended to keep to the far side of the enclosure away from humans and the much used lower tracks.

There were very few chases within the pack, but Manchas and later Dourado with him, patrolled the fence bordering on the track separating MIIB from MIIA. The energy which Manchas devoted to patrolling this section of the fence - some 100m which he raced up and down - keeping pace with his rival Sandalo on the other side, was astonishing and left one in no doubt of the cardinal importance of the possession of territory in the wolf's psyche.

Commentary

The importance of territory has been much remarked and need not be stressed. A wolf evidently feels just as possessive of his land in captivity as he does in the wild. Why, then, does he not scent-mark the boundary? (When

Sandalo, Manchas and Morena were temporarily transferred to a then unoccupied MIIB Sandalo immediately set about scent-marking. He did this thoroughly and for some time - but he did not do it along or close to the fence.) The simplest explanation is to suppose that he considers that it is not necessary - the fence does it for him. But the explanation is more psychologically complex because a wolf's territory is in practice wherever he is. A cage, if he is placed in one, is his territory which he will vigorously defend. It goes even beyond that, for, in the last analysis, territory is personal space. We begin with our bodies and our clothing; go on to our immediate surroundings and essential personal possessions, and expand, or not as the case may be, to the acquisition of property of one kind or another. And property conveys status on wolves as on men. Thus a wolf who leaves the pack goes in search of his own territory without which he cannot eat - or find a mate. In the same way, man must find a job and somewhere to live before he can find a wife and reproduce.

In the case of our three packs this feeling was of course innate in each pack and every individual component. The differences are due only to the different surroundings and the activities they encouraged or prevented. The territory in each case dominated pack and individual behaviour. When Sandalo and Fosco were both removed to be vasectomised, they were kept for a week in small adjacent enclosures. Each defended his small plot as though it were his birthright. Fosco, who, "at home" always deferred to his chief, now defied him, growling at him through the fence. Yet, when I paid Fosco a visit, he glanced first at Sandalo to see if it was safe to come up to me to be caressed.

The wolves, in all three packs, tended to make territories-within-territories, small sections of the area which became their favourite refuges. This applied more to subordinates than to the elite, except during Deneb's reign in MI, when he and Neb reserved a space of their own. In MIIA there was a general desire to rest near the alphas on the slope, but rank prevailed here too. The more senior you were, the nearer to Sandalo you could recline.

Personally, I much regret the necessity of keeping wolves or any wild animals in captivity, but, based on my observations of these wolves I am quite sure that they regarded, and in two cases regard these enclosures as their home. When escapes occurred the escapees did not stray far from base and, in one case, returned and were easily persuaded to re-enter. But we must not forget that there is a love of freedom balanced by a fear of it. I shall never forget how a friend of mine, imprisoned in a cage by the Gestapo, and a fervent lover of freedom, found it very hard, when he was at last set free, to step out into the world. Our feeling for territory expands to fill the space available until it reaches the limit of our capacity or is arrested by agoraphobia. So we should never think of captivity as anything but a *pis aller*.

Lastly, tensions arise in packs which find a natural resolution in the wild but which must often require human intervention in captive facilities. This was never done in MI with unfortunate results. It has never been necessary in MIIB. In MIIA omega wolves have been removed when persecution passed the point of no return. This was only possible because backup enclosures existed so that the wolves could be suitably rehomed. I have heard it said, by those who ought to know better, that the loss of omega wolves through persecution is unfortunate but must be accepted because it is "nature". We must never forget that captivity is not "nature", and its consequences are often unnatural.

Part IV

The Wolves as Individuals

The fact that all these wolves lived in comparable circumstances and situations casts their individual differences - their personalities - into clear relief.

In his own pack Deneb was always the most individual and striking of the wolves. He gave the impression of being a born leader; his authority was absolute and, during his unfortunately short life, was never challenged. He was so self-confident that he never felt the need to assert his dominance except, briefly, during the courtship season. As his treatment of the omega wolf, Carina, proved, he was also extremely tolerant. It is most unusual for an alpha to show such restraint in the treatment of an omega animal. Towards his chosen mate, Musca, he was always tender and solicitous; he went out of his way to ensure her welfare, especially during her pregnancies and later, the birth of her pups. His close and unbroken friendship with his brother, Neb, was very touching; they quite obviously loved each other, so obviously that I found myself mentally comparing them to David and Jonathan! He did not assert his dominance, even at feeding times, but allowed his brother to precede him, and later, encouraged his offspring, especially Rigel, to come and help themselves.

To begin with he was also prepared to be friendly with humans - there were occasional visitors - but as he grew older he became more and more wary. Only with me did he remain friendly until his death. Except during the breeding season, when he was otherwise occupied and ignored me completely, he would always come up to greet me if I approached, would take food, very delicately, from my hand, and would sometimes then turn his back to me, lie down and go to sleep; there can be no greater mark of trust. If he saw me in one of my hiding-places he would show that he had recognised me, would give no warning wuff but carry on with what whatever he was doing. He was the only member of that pack who truly became my friend.

His counterpart in MIIA, Sandalo, was even more individual; he, too, was a born leader but, although his authority was just as absolute and has never been challenged, he was for some reason less sure of himself and found it necessary to be far more assertive, forcing submissions, especially from his beta male, on frequent occasions (and not only during the courtship season) and in general losing no chance to show "who was boss". Similarly, he was much less tolerant than Deneb and his treatment of the omega animals - during the course of my observations there were four of these - showed none of the restraint or easy-going live and let live that distinguished Deneb's treatment of Carina. Although not as solicitous of Morena's welfare during pregnancy as Deneb had been with Musca's, he spent far more time in her company; until illness overcame her, they were virtually inseparable and together they carried out tasks - patrols and the like - which in MI were done by Deneb and Neb. He never showed for Manchas the deep friendship that Deneb showed for Neb; on the contrary, he and Morena made it clear that he was subordinate to them and eventually turned against him and, in effect, expelled him. In this or, at least, in the position and authority he accepted in his mate, he was more "orthodox" than Deneb who was, in this respect at least, more original.

From the very beginning, as a pup, Sandalo had been the dominant animal at feeding times and he remained so, asserting his right by growling and, if necessary, assaulting, those whom hunger drove to dispute his priority. He was as concerned to feed the pups as Deneb had been but his concern did not last so long, except for his patronage of Onor, which found no parallel in MI until Hamal "adopted" Regulus.

For the first two years Sandalo was very friendly towards almost all humans. As time passed he became less so; he also became more discriminating. But comparisons here are of small value, for Sandalo was reared by humans and for many years had human visitors. I, too, spent far more time with him, in his enclosure, than I was ever able to do with Deneb. In many ways, however, their attitudes to me were similar. Sandalo, too, would come to greet me, would put his forepaws on my shoulders and lick my face, would take food, likewise with the greatest delicacy, from my hand, and would turn his back on me and go about his business without giving the matter further thought. He was also tolerant of a certain Senhor João, who had been a shepherd in the north of the country before coming to work at the IWRC; but Senhor João, like myself, had helped to rear these pups and entered the enclosure almost every day, to clean it or maintain the fences.

Sandalo also showed great intelligence (in the conventional sense of that word). "You can see him thinking", a volunteer worker once remarked when Sandalo and Morena were working out how to penetrate a section of fence! He was so intelligent as to cause some alarm and motivate the staff to strengthen his enclosure. Deneb, by comparison, seemed "wiser" but less clever and, although his fence was just as vulnerable, he made no attempt to escape or even test its weaknesses.

The other alpha male - when he became alpha - Manchas, was in a different category. Never a born leader, he became one only through human intervention. Despite his size and strength, he seemed to be more of a "born subordinate", but, as soon as he was provided with a mate (his sister, Clarinha) and a territory, he rose to the occasion well enough. He lacks the self-confidence of either Deneb or Sandalo, however, and, as already noted, spends much of his time defending his territory against a supposed threat from his old leader. He is demonstrably as devoted to Clarinha as either of the other two to their mates, but less solicitous for her welfare - he's more of an egoist! He began by loving human company but, after Clarinha's first litter was born he became more and more wary. He did not threaten unwelcome humans as did Sandalo, however; he simply ran off at the sight of them. Eventually he only welcomed me and even this he did less effusively after Clarinha's second litter was born. No doubt his temporary segregation and the removal of his pups two years running did not endear men to him. He was surprisingly timid. He was the only wolf who remained behind in the enclosure during the first, pack escape in 1992. On another occasion I was standing in MIIB and he and Clarinha were close to the fence, in front of me, when some visitors appeared, walking towards us. The wolves watched them intently but, as they drew near, Manchas became afraid. Leaving his sister by the fence he retreated fast, not, as I would have expected, into the heather, but to take refuge behind me, with his head resting against my thigh. This proof that he still regarded me as his protector filled me with a strange feeling. He was childish and never really grew up. I think he was what we should call backward, or "simple-minded", which may account for his initial demotion. He loved to play but, unlike his brother Sandalo he was very rough - I often had difficulty to keep my feet. Even so, he was basically gentle. When a Portuguese assistant went in and began to play with him he (the man) became rougher and rougher - a "macho" display - and eventually threw Manchas down so that he fell hard and rolled over. He was of course on his feet again in an instant, but only to shake himself and return for more. Had I been the wolf I would have gone for the man. Despite his weaknesses - or perhaps because of them - Manchas was much loved.

These weaknesses may explain his eventual failure as a beta male. He provides a strong contrast with the MI beta, Neb. He proved to be the perfect beta male. He never challenged Deneb and always gave him full support. He seemed to delight in his brother's company and spent almost all his time with him. He was more tolerant of Carina than even Deneb was and he showed great affection for Musca. He was also the wildest of the wolves. It is always harder to form a clear impression of the personality of a beta animal because his character is subservient to his social role and his real potential will only become apparent if he is required to take over the leadership. As the beta male Neb was loyal, friendly, playful and self-effacing. He was also very conscientious, especially with the pups. But I mostly remember the tremendous play sessions with his brother which, especially in Winter, were daily occurrences. For as much as a half hour they would chase and romp all over the area and splash in the deep puddles that were formed by the rains. I never saw any of the other wolves play like this - whether they were pups, yearlings or, as in this case, adults.

After Manchas was demoted and removed from the pack Fosco became the beta male, but a less self-assured and more tentative one than either Manchas or Neb. But Fosco is very different from either of them. Timid and cautious from puphood, he is also subtler than any of the others. Conscious of a certain vulnerability he perhaps developed or evolved forms of psychological defence. To my mind, the wolf he most resembled, in this respect, was Vega, but he was more successful. He was (and is) very observant, very intelligent, able to make an accurate "appreciation of the situation" and to take appropriate action. This has enabled him to avoid or attenuate many for him dangerous situations and to escape serious persecution. He is also favoured by great physical beauty and, in our eyes, charm. I had a long relationship with him. As he was restricted by his chief, we communicated with signals. Unlike the other males, he became more fond of humans as he grew older, as he showed when Sandalo's absence made it possible for him to approach them. His position of beta male has now become even more tentative with the rise of Onor, but he continues to be a member of what has become the leading - male - trio. Fosco is in fact a successful opportunist, but a particularly charming one.

As a pup Hamal showed no signs of his later eminence; he was so seldom seen that I had hardly any impression of him. Later, after his sudden development, he became forceful and energetic in the pack but remained shyer of me than his subordinates. He was a magnificently handsome wolf, if not as beautiful as the grey and silver Neb, but his personality was less attractive than his father Deneb's; he was a less tolerant and less distinguished leader. Almost his whole time was devoted to his mate, unlike Deneb, who divided his between Musca and his duties as pack leader. As a result the pack, under Hamal, became, as such, less of an organism than it had been under Deneb's rule. For the first few months of 1989 it even appeared to be split into two nuclei: a central nucleus, composed of Hamal, Ara and Altair, and a subordinate and much looser nucleus, containing Rigel, Vega and Musca. After the birth of the fourth generation, however, the pack once more closed ranks to some extent and its form became more orthodox; as usual the birth of pups pulled things together. Hamal's most striking feature was his lifelong devotion to his mate Ara; he was more constantly with her than ever Deneb was with Musca. He also proved to be a most concerned and caring father, showing the same tenderness for his only pup, Regulus, as has Sandalo shown for Onor. His relations with his beta males, Rigel first, and then Altair and Thuban, have been less friendly and more attenuated than those of Deneb/Neb or, now, Manchas/Dourado. But it is hard for an alpha male to fulfil 100% both functions, of pack leader and spouse; as he is, so he chooses.

Hamal's brother, Rigel, although a less successful wolf, was a more interesting personality. I was able to observe him better, too, because he had much less fear of me and a better understanding of my intentions and movements. At first I expected him to succeed Deneb as Pack leader; like his father he seemed to be a born leader, but his injury at a critical time may have prevented his promotion. Whatever the cause, he accepted his brother's preferment with dignity and without resentment, indeed with what I can only call grace. After his demotion from beta male to a subordinate position, he became a quiet, somewhat aloof and very attractive wolf. His love for and devotion to his sister, Vega, was notable and gave rise to a most revealing incident.

Among the many harassing actions which I witnessed in that pack, one in particular has remained in my memory. Vega, hard pressed by a mob of nine wolves, took up a defensive stance with her back to the fence and defended herself valiantly. The others were to some extent hampered by their own numbers and could not get behind her to attack her hindquarters. Nevertheless, when they abandoned the assault and dispersed into the bush, Vega was visibly exhausted. She took a few paces forward and sat, haunched and panting, under the branches of an olive tree. For a short time she was the only wolf in sight. Then Rigel came out of cover - he had not taken part in the action against her - walked up to her and stood close. First, he pressed his right cheek to her right cheek, then his left to her left. He then moved round and sat on his haunches at her side. Rigel's actions had no apparent function. They did not benefit him - on the contrary, for he ran the risk of "punishment" - but only his sister, who was comforted. The only sensible and simple explanation is to assume that he acted out of compassion, a quality usually denied to animals, especially wild ones. But there are long-term, as well as the more obvious short-term, means to successful survival. And if this behaviour of Rigel's can occur in captivity it can also occur in the wild. So, wolves know compassion. The fact that this particular form of it has never been observed so far as I know, need not detain us. The sight of one black swan suffices to refute the proposition that "All swans are white".

Of Vega herself I have already written enough, while her sister, Ara, was so frightened of humans, a fear which long familiarity with my presence never overcame, that I was left with no better understanding of her character than as a slighter mirror-image of her mate, Hamal. For similar reasons I was unable to make in-depth studies of the other subordinate females, or males, in this pack, and the same reservation applies to those in the other two packs. Subordinates are usually to some extent inhibited in the self-expression which reveals character and those who were not hand-reared or habituated to human presence are additionally too elusive and retiring to justly observe.

Musca, fortunately, is another matter. Although so shy, her leading position forced her into the open where her actions and reactions revealed a distinct and distinguished personality. Her latent strength of character surfaced when she confidently assumed the leadership after Deneb's death and held it, firmly, efficiently, tolerantly and gracefully for eighteen months. Her initial fear of all humans, too, gradually diminished and, happily, she became progressively less wary of me until, in 1989, she ceased altogether to avoid me and seek cover, despite the fact that she had lost her alpha status or, more accurately, had wisely ceded it to her son, Hamal. Musca was strong, but she was at the same time gentle. unassertive and unaggressive. I saw her occasionally assert her dominance during her alphahood, but this she did with the restraint that comes from strength. I never saw her harass another animal and her refusal to take part in the chasing and persecution of Carina was most notable and completely "unorthodox". I have several times watched a chase in which Carina, closely pursued by Deneb and Neb, rushed past within an inch of Musca's nose. She took no notice whatever. As a widow and an ex-alpha she for some time led a rather aloof existence as a subordinate. Later, her health deteriorated and she retired altogether from pack life and passed her time alone. It was during this autumnal period that she communed with herself in the touching way I have already described. To the end she gave a strong impression of gentleness, patience and dignity. It is rightly said that in nature and the animal world there is neither right nor wrong, good nor bad. Animals just are. Yet, of all these wolves, Musca is the one to whom it is hardest to deny the moral quality of goodness. She seemed to occupy a niche between animal and human.

Despite her social role Carina was never quite as nervous of me as Musca initially was, but her wariness increased or diminished in step with the degree of harassment she had to endure. She is hard to describe because her actions and personality were so curtailed and suppressed by her fate. I do not know why she should have been cast, so early on, in the omega role, especially as her alpha sister played no part in the choice; the explanation may be as simple as that Deneb liked Musca and did not like her, but, once established, there was no going back. I find my feeling about her best expressed by Loren Eiseley:

"But I do love the world ... I love its small ones, the things beaten into the strangling surf; the bird, singing, which falls and is not seen again...I love the lost ones, the failures of this world". So much for my feelings, but there seems to be a psychological explanation of the omega phenomenon, when the occasion does not result from one of the overtly functional causes. The presence of a hanger-on, for example, may, as in immature human groups, serve to define and strengthen the group's identity and cohesion or, as William Horwood has expressed it so compassionately in his tale, *The Wolves of Time*: "Her very exclusion made them feel more united so that, paradoxically, she began to have a role".

Unlike Musca, Morena was a stern alpha female, establishing her ascendancy by putting down, keeping down and finally ostracising her only rival, Clarinha. She could be stern, too, with males and was the first to begin the marginalisation of Manchas. She was perfectly orthodox in that she was responsible for the female SRO. Inevitably, too, she differed from Musca in that she had been hand-reared and was thoroughly habituated to humans. She liked humans, too, and rarely rejected their friendly advances. From a very few, always men, she fled and they were men whose body language exhibited their suppressed aggression. She much preferred the company of her own kind, however, when she could have it, which was not always possible after her removal from the pack. During Manchas's brief segregation and sojourn with her she was so happy to have his company that she forgot all about her human friends and ignored them. When Manchas had to be tranquillised and was then returned to her, she butted the man who brought Manchas back in the forehead. With all this she was highly intelligent and was surely responsible for initiating the pack's brief escape in 1992. She was also, despite her innate physical weaknesses, astonishingly lithe and athletic. When she was alone I and others used to play with her and were astonished at the tremendous leaps across hollows and over bushes that she took. She was an excellent mother and proved to be just as protective of others' pups. After her removal from the pack her enclosure bordered on the small one in which the hand-reared pups from Clarinha's first litter were briefly homed. Morena was so protective of them, barking her defiance at any staff member who entered to attend to the pups, and trying to tunnel under the wire in order to join them, that she had to be temporarily removed to an adjacent enclosure so that the volunteers could work in peace and safety. Although she may lack what I can only call Musca's moral grace, Morena stood out as an exceptionally fine specimen of her race and needs no greater testimony than the love and respect which she received and receives from all who come into contact with her.

Clarinha suffered much under Morena although there was nothing "unnatural" in the treatment she received; it was her captivity which was unnatural, and its consequences those responsible for her welfare were able to mitigate. Once removed from her natal pack - in the wild she would surely have removed herself - she flourished. Physically she was much healthier than Morena, although she was not as strong or "tough". She was as devoted a mate and just as caring and conscientious a mother. She also showed great ingenuity in deceiving humans as to the whereabouts of her dens or growing pups. She delighted in human company and only became wary of them, with good reason, after the removal of some of her pups. After that, perhaps aware that I had had no part in it, she reserved her trust for me and allowed me every liberty. She wore her alphahood easily and I never saw her behave harshly to her pups. A gentle, loveable creature. Why, then, did Morena prevail over her? Partly because these matters are decided very early on and, once decided, are difficult to reverse. Also, no doubt, because Sandalo chose her. But mostly, I think, because Clarinha was too gentle. This is ideal in the small pack she now helps to lead; in a larger unit or, still more, in the wild, this must be a disadvantage. There, leaders must be tough - and Morena is tough. Once again, it comes down to personality.

None of her successors inherited Morena's force of character. Zef is the most outstanding and the only one, in Morena's absence, to earn Sandalo's tolerance and even respect. Early on she attracted my attention by the way she reconnoitred the position before approaching the food. She had, of course, to wait her turn, but she did this in a poised and intelligent manner. And she inveigled her way into Sandalo's good graces - and into the alpha position - with considerable tact and, having once obtained her objective, behaved towards her less fortunate rivals with restraint. Had she not been Sandalo's daughter - and no wolf can succeed Morena in Sandalo's eyes - she might well occupy a more prominent place in the pack than she now does.

In order to understand the role of personality and the need for individuality in a wolf pack - essential for hunting in the wild - we must recognise that in this there is a very effective balance between freedom and responsibility. If we look back over the various episodic relationships I have recorded we find that wolves have personal feelings of kinship and affection very like our own, but that these are always subordinated to the higher good of the pack, of wolf society and, therefore, of the survival of the species. Thus Manchas as beta male could join in the persecution of Clarinha and then, later on and in other circumstances, become her devoted mate, while Sandalo could enjoy what promised to be a monogamous bond with Morena until her indisposition and resulting absence demanded the sacrifice of his own inclinations in the interests of society. Had he been a wolf, Britain's Edward VIII would not have abdicated in favour of Mrs Simpson!

All the wolves constantly surprised me. Their behaviour was only predictable to a limited extent and within the general outlines of their society, but within this framework there is room and need for great behavioural variations and these are perhaps even more apparent with captive animals which, as they do not have to earn their living, concentrate their energies on social relationships. The needs of wolf society are only truly met by the development of individual personality such as we have seen in the examples cited above and in the course of this study.

Afterword

Beyond The Wire

Our nearest relative in the animal world is said to be the chimpanzee. Genetically speaking this may be so, but socially and psychologically I think we are much closer to the wolf. Perhaps this is why, for thousands of years, we have enjoyed a symbiotic relationship with the wolf's descendent, the domestic dog. It may also be one of the reasons why we have chosen the wolf as our scapegoat, forcing it to bear the burden of the unacceptable and therefore rejected elements in our psyche and consequently persecuted it - and continue to persecute it - to the edge of extinction. But this only compounds our psycho-neurosis. It is time we grew up and found the courage and integrity to recognise and withdraw our projections. We cannot be alienated and whole. Watching and being with the wolves helped me to find the wolf, and to find myself.

As Loren Eiseley has written: "One does not meet oneself until one catches the reflection in an eye other than human". Because its special relationship with man has for so long been negative (though not always or with all peoples) the wolf is a test case. If we can take back our projections and see ourselves - and the wolves - with honesty, this could mark the beginning of our redemption and of the return from exile of the outcasts from Eden that we are.

In recent years many people have found comfort and healing in the company of orcas and dolphins. I can testify that the company of wolves is also therapeutic. Land mammals like ourselves, they are at one and the same time wild, orderly and inwardly calm. Watching them, being with them, the troubled mind subsides to "alpha waves", the troubled heart finds peace beside the clear waters of the river of life.

I believe that the purpose of existence on earth is to be what one is, this is the true function and the fundamental right of all living beings and upon this all our morality and ethics should be based. In our case, this imperative almost certainly demands a lifetime dedicated to becoming what one is, but the animals do not have to undertake this inner journey, they are already there.

Part V

Tables

Table 1. MI - Family Tree

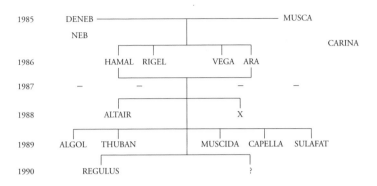

Table 2. MIIA - Family Tree

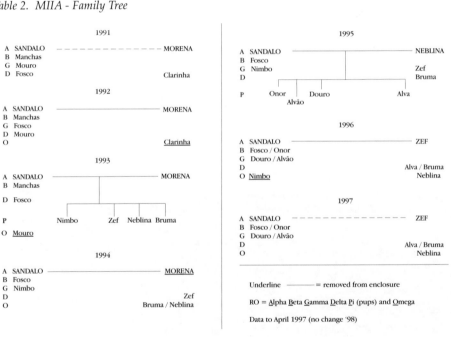

Table 3. MIIB - Family Tree   *MIIB - Evolution SRO*

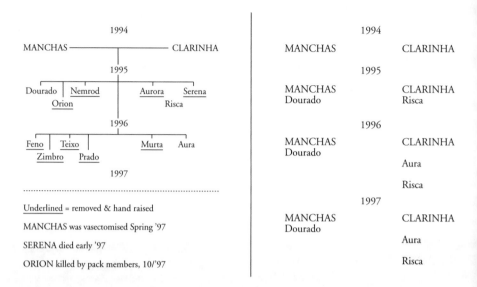

Underlined = removed & hand raised

MANCHAS was vasectomised Spring '97

SERENA died early '97

ORION killed by pack members, 10/'97

Table 4. MI - Estimated reproduction and reproduction in all three packs

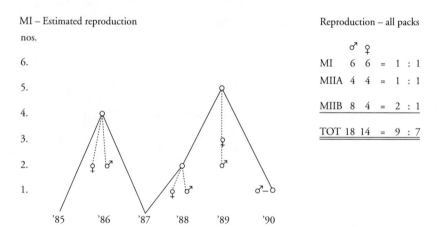

Table 5. MIIA - Population dynamics

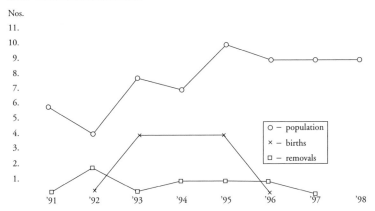

MIIA – POPULATION DYNAMICS

Nos.

○ – population
× – births
□ – removals

'91   '92   '93   '94   '95   '96   '97   '98

Table 6. MIIB - Population dynamics and reproduction

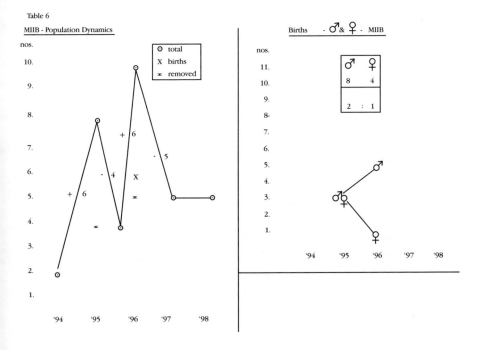

Table 6

MIIB - Population Dynamics

nos.

○ total
X births
✱ removed

Births   - ♂& ♀ - MIIB

nos.

♂	♀
8	4
2	:	1

'94   '95   '96   '97   '98

Table 7. *Reproduction, Alpha and Beta packs (MIIA/B)*

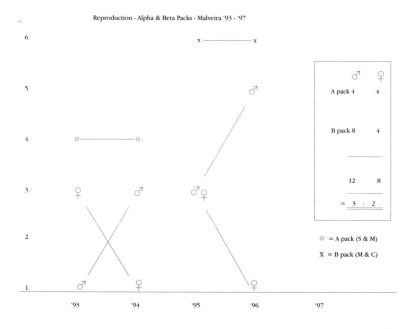

Reproduction - Alpha & Beta Packs - Malveira '93 - '97

Table 8. *MI - Changes in the SRO 1984 -1990*

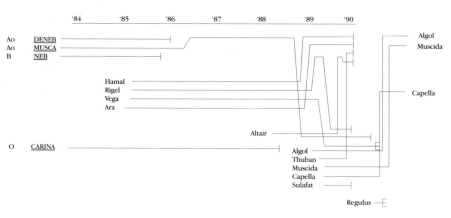

MI : changes in the SRO, 1984 - 1990

Legend: underlined = died

⎯⎯| = removed   ⎯E = escaped and was shot

Table 9. MIIA - Changes in the SRO 1991-1998

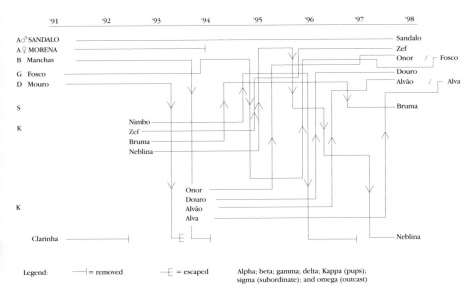

Legend: ──┤ = removed   ──Ε = escaped   Alpha; beta; gamma; delta; Kappa (pups);
sigma (subordinate); and omega (outcast)

MIIA : changes in the SRO, June, '91 to May, 1998

Table 10. MIIB - Changes in the SRO 1994-1998

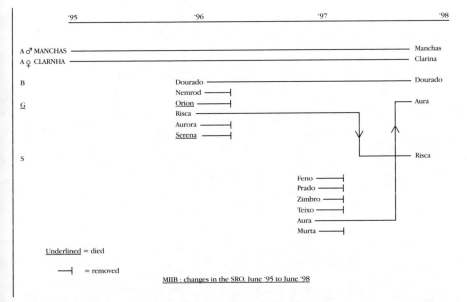

Underlined = died

──┤ = removed

MIIB : changes in the SRO, June '95 to June '98

References

(1) Schenkel, R. 1947. Ausdrucksstudien an Wölfen. (Quoted in Zimen, E. (v. infra.)).

(2) Zimen, E. 1975. Social Dynamics in the Wolf Pack. In The Wild Canids. ed. M. Fox. New York. Litton Publishers.

(3) Mech, L. David. 1970. The Wolf. New York. Doubleday.

(4) Magalhães, C.P. 1975. Aspectos do Lobo em Portugal. XII Congresso da União Internacional dos Biologistos da Caça. Tema VII., and van Haaften, J.L. 1982. The Bragança-Zamora Wolf Project (cyclostyled).

(5) Zimen, E. 1981. The Wolf. Souvenir Press. London.

(6) Harrington, Fred H. 1986. Wolves & Humans. Vol. 1. Wolf Vocalisations. The Science Museum of Minnesota.

(7) Lawrence, R.D. 1986. In Praise of Wolves. Collins. Toronto.